D1015149

GIVE US
OUR DREAM

GIVE US OUR DREAM

by

Arthémise Goertz

WHITTLESEY HOUSE

McGRAW-HILL BOOK COMPANY, INC.

NEW YORK : LONDON

GIVE US OUR DREAM

The author wishes to express her gratitude to Harper & Brothers for permission to quote from Thomas Hardy's novel, "Tess of the D'Urbervilles," published by that firm.

PUBLISHED BY WHITTLESEY HOUSE
A division of the McGraw-Hill Book Company, Inc.

PRINTED IN THE UNITED STATES OF AMERICA

TO MY MOTHER

Part I

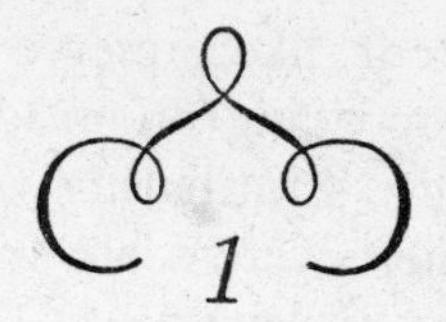

IT WAS one of those two-story brick buildings, built like a box. There was a row of stores underneath, and over them a set of apartments, four front and four back, separated by a hall. A stairway cascaded from the hall down into a vestibule which opened on the street.

When Mr. Kennedy came to collect the rent he never failed to say: "Nice little apartments, don't you think? We have others out here on Long Island that are nicer, but they're forty-five minutes from town, while these in Sunnyside are only thirty from Times Square."

Mrs. Lily Marsan always smiled. "Very nice," she would agree, handing over her forty dollars. As a matter of fact, she hardly ever went to Times Square. It meant much more to her that the apartments were across the street from the gas station and the tavern.

The gas station was closed now, of course, because it was two o'clock in the morning; but the tavern was as lively as fireworks. Mrs. Marsan could see only the kitchen end, no matter which way she screwed Mr. Cernak's opera glasses, since the tavern stood behind the gas station, facing the Sixty-eighth Street side of a triangle. The windows were lit up as if the place were on fire and juke box music was pouring out in hot noisy blasts. Cars were parked so close together in the lot behind the kitchen that it looked as if they had been stacked there.

Mrs. Marsan scanned the cars and deplored the fact that

they were not transparent, like preserve jars. She knew things better than sweets were going on inside. It was a Saturday night in autumn—spicy, scintillating October. The air was tangy and cool, and there were more stars than sky. It was a night for exciting things to happen.

Sitting in the dark of her bedroom window with Lady on her lap, Mrs. Marsan waited for them to start. She could not have said whether she hoped or feared something might happen like night before last. A couple had come over from the tavern to pet on Sig's newspaper stand directly under her window. She could even hear them talk—though they had precious little to say. "Honey" and "Handsome," they called each other. They were there about half an hour when the skimpy little man found them. He came tearing through the parked cars and across the street, terrible as a tornado. There was no policeman around. They never were around when they should be.

The furious little fellow appeared in the middle of a kiss so prolonged that it looked to Mrs. Marsan as if the pair were in a coma. The woman was lying in her companion's arms, her head thrown back on his shoulder so that the line of her throat was a white curve, the fingers of one hand buried in his fair wavy hair. The woman had no time to straighten, and her good-looking boy friend was pinned down by her weight and his own surprise. Spitting out a mouthful of language that took Mrs. Marsan's breath away, the intruder jerked the woman to her feet and swung her lunging against the mailbox on the curb. For a snarling moment the two men faced each other, standing with ready fists. The dashing lover was half a head taller and a full foot broader than his scrap of an enemy.

Mrs. Marsan had a dim memory of having added a short scream of her own to Honey's as the little man's arm shot out and up in a swift hard aim. Honey yelled "*Jim!*" in a voice to reach heaven and rushed in between them, but he hurled her aside. Handsome's blow caught him on the jaw, sent him staggering toward the street, but he bounded back like a spring, closing Handsome's eye with a punch Mrs. Marsan could hear. Handsome was bigger, but Jim was faster, and the two men smashed away at each other, grunting and gasping, while Honey screamed and hugged the mailbox in terror. Mrs. Marsan wanted to do something—run or call for help—but her legs and throat felt locked. Presently a dark wet smear spread on Handsome's mouth where just a while before Honey's kiss had clung. As his right fist came down in a blind rage, Jim stepped aside, then jumped in with a blow that struck Handsome between the eyes and whipped him off his feet. Mrs. Marsan trembled at the sound of it, followed by Handsome's crash to the pavement and another scream from Honey. Then it was all over. Handsome lay quite still and Honey hugged the mailbox harder and began to talk and cry hysterically.

At the tavern the juke box blared carelessly on, but here in the building everybody was up, and it was Sig who had telephoned for the police. It was hard to tell how badly Handsome was hurt. Just this morning Sig furnished her the last of the details in the case, relayed by Donegan, the policeman on the daytime beat.

"Understand the big beauty's lost his looks. Busted nose," Sig said. "Would you of thought the little guy packed such a wallop?" Some friend saw Jim's wife at the tavern and tipped him off, Sig explained. "He'd been suspicious a long time—she was never home any more."

"She's home still less now," Mrs. Marsan guessed. "The way those two were carrying on, I bet she's haunting the hospital."

"Hospital hell," Sig sneered. "She's haunting the jail-house. Between the best looker and the best fighter, a woman'll take the hero any time. She's in love with her husband all over again."

Mrs. Marsan was not sure whether or not she agreed with Sig, but she agreed with the way things turned out. Cranks could say what they wanted about taverns being the cesspools of society and a menace to morals. But if there had been no tavern there would have been no fight, and if there had been no fight there would have been no renewed romance between Honey and Jim. A broken nose was easier mended than a broken home. . . .

Lately Nick Dinapolis had been talking about closing the tavern and going to Florida, but Mrs. Marsan wished fervently he never would. It was bad enough when the gas station was vacant all that time during the war. Now it had come to life again with cars drawing up to the bright red pumps and men jumping out to tap tires and women in slacks or fur coats bossing the mechanics around or yelling at the kids not to let the dog out. If the tavern ever closed— Mrs. Marsan shuddered at the thought. . . .

For years now Mrs. Marsan had suffered joyously from insomnia. She was no longer sure whether it was an affliction or an accomplishment. She knew only that she never thought of going to bed before three or four in the morning. For her, midnight and the early hours were washed away into eternity with cups of coffee—when the weather grew chill, black coffee sporting a dash of rum or brandy. She had no patience with people who read detective stories or took pills to put them to sleep. They had the gift of wakefulness and they threw it in the garbage.

Things happened at night that never happened in the daytime. Night was a different country. Customs were different, clothes were different, feelings were different. Life was a night-blooming cereus; it shriveled up in the day when people had to work and worry. Daytime was the gas station—tools clanking on concrete, oil smells, cars backfiring and wheezing and honking, voices shouting. That was interesting, but not exciting. Nighttime—that was the tavern. Music and food and drinking inside, and outside the cars and the couples, and the loving and laughing. . . .

Mrs. Marsan yawned. She was not drowsy, but becoming bored. She scratched behind Lady's poodle ears with one hand while the other held the opera glasses to unrewarded eyes. This was going to be one of those dull nights, after all. Nothing visible was going to happen. Sometimes it was like that. You had to expect to draw a blank once in a while. The clock in the next room hammered out the seconds, forging the hour. It must be nearly three. Unless a lively act came on soon she might as well leave her box seat and go to bed.

A boy and girl emerged from the tangle of cars behind the tavern and walked over to the bus stop. They stood there waiting under the street light. Mrs. Marsan trained the glasses on them hungrily. There was not even a shadow between her and the stage now. But when was the play going to start? There they stood, straight and steady as two pickets in a fence. "Sober," Mrs. Marsan said to herself disgustedly. The bus drew up and absorbed them.

That settled it. She was going to bed. If there were any indications of drama she would have gone back to the kitchen and made herself more coffee, but tonight's show was a flop and she might as well ring down the curtain. A big Saturday, too. And with stars like that. . . .

Mrs. Marsan realized so suddenly that something was happening on the sidewalk under her window that she jumped up out of her chair, spilling Lady on the floor. A taxi was at the curb, and a woman was paying the driver. The glasses brought her up to the window sill where Mrs. Marsan could examine her in detail, even though dimly.

She was young. Tall and slim. Too slim. "She don't look

prosperous," Mrs. Marsan observed under her breath. It was hard to tell—everything had an air of secrecy at night, that was half the fun of it—but her suit appeared shabby and she had a droopy, down-at-the-heel air all over. "She's skinny," Mrs. Marsan thought. The girl picked up her overnight case and turned toward the building, while the taxi arrowed down the street. She stood still for a moment and looked up, right into the opera glasses. Mrs. Marsan slipped behind the curtains, carrying a swift impression of a pale face and shoulder-length hair, straight and tawny.

She was coming in. Mrs. Marsan could not see which one of the eight buttons down there the girl was pushing, and she failed to hear if anybody buzzed the door open. Maybe from the other window she could see better. . . . She went quickly to the living room. Puffing from the effort of hurrying excessive flesh even so short a space, she unhooked the screen and leaned out a little. The girl downstairs was fumbling with a key. So she had a key. . . .

Her steps could be heard on the stairway—fearful, phantom steps. They went past, softly as falling leaves. Before Mrs. Marsan could cross the room for a look into the hall, she heard a door discreetly close. She stuck her head out. There was nobody.

She was about to retire without knowing where the girl went when she noticed the light fanning out from under Mr. Ingalls' door.

Mr. Ingalls was the bachelor in the fourth apartment back. When a young woman with an overnight case sneaked up around three o'clock in the morning and the only light in the hall came from under his door, it was easy to guess whose key she had. . . .

Mrs. Marsan did not begrudge him. On the contrary, she was glad he had something in his life besides work. Mr. Ingalls was the nicest manager the neighborhood A&P ever had

—drudged all day getting other people fed and stayed home every evening, quiet and invisible as air, until everybody wondered what he did in there all by himself. Mrs. Marsan laughed softly. Sly fox. He was less alone than he looked.

She remembered now. This was not the first time she had seen light seeping from under Mr. Ingalls' door late at night or in the early dark hours of the new day. A pleasant shiver went through her. All that excitement going on just across the hall, when she was searching the streets for it. That's the way things were—right under your nose and you didn't smell them.

It was going to be a good Saturday show after all. She decided to drip a fresh pot of coffee and sit up and wait for the finale when the girl came out.

Mrs. Marsan went into the kitchen and set the water on the stove to boil.

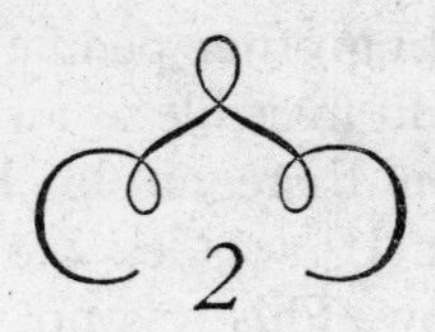

Mr. Joseph Cernak always dropped in for a cup at four o'clock on Sunday afternoons. It was the hour of elegance in Mrs. Marsan's week—the social event for which she polished what was left of the silver on her plated ware and put out her initialed napkins. His sister Jessamine, when she was herself, came with him. They lived in 2-F, the second apartment front, separated from Mrs. Marsan's by the stairs.

Today Mr. Cernak was late. It was nearly five when his familiar rap, light as rain, was heard on the door. Jessamine was with him, but she was only half herself. She towered behind him, the usual green chiffon veil floating about her throat.

Mrs. Marsan liked to stand beside Jessamine. It gave her the sensation of being petite. Today, in her brown georgette hostess that reached to her ankles, she felt faylike by comparison, even without the constricting help of corsets. But at the side of Mr. Cernak she underwent an abrupt reversal, as if she were looking in one of those crazy mirrors that magnify the human figure to grotesque surprises. She felt broad and bloated, and wished she had at least put on a brassière.

Mr. Cernak was a splinter of a man with sparse gray hair that fell in fronds over the left side of his forehead. His eyes were sky blue, like Jessamine's, but while hers were practically always blurred, his were practically always bright. It was difficult to believe that Jessamine was his older sister

—if only by two years—for at fifty Mr. Cernak, except for his eyes, had the faded frailty of ash, while Jessamine, her six amazonian feet topped by a magnificent stack of red hair, was as arresting as flame.

"You shouldn't have waited," Mr. Cernak said. "We're unforgivably late."

He sat in his usual chair, the one with the loose arm. He would have been lost in the overstuffed.

"Not unforgivably." Mrs. Marsan smiled graciously, and poured him a cup of coffee. "And I didn't wait. I've had two already."

"I thought the doctor told you not to drink so much." Mr. Cernak looked at Mrs. Marsan over his cup, gently reproving.

"The doctor can go to blazes. To blazes, I tell you!" Jessamine got up out of the overstuffed and shrieked, "I'll drink as much as I please!"

"What made you late?" Mrs. Marsan asked. Though it was remarkable that such an effect could be achieved, it was just as if Jessamine were not there.

"I went to a meeting. It was wonderful."

"It's loathsome. Loathsome, I tell you." Jessamine sipped her coffee and made a face.

"Did they decide on the revolution?" Mrs. Marsan passed the cakes.

"*Not* revolution," Mr. Cernak corrected for the dozenth time. "*Revaluation.* I thought I'd explained it." He put his cup down and prepared patiently to explain again.

"I'm thirsty." Jessamine made a queer snorting noise as if she were strangling.

"A total revaluation of the social and economic setup throughout the country," Mr. Cernak continued, "whereby the dignity of man would be placed at least on a par with the present artificial importance of money, materials and machines. A just plan for the proper partition of wealth. *Sharing* with the masses, not *shearing* them."

"That would make a good slogan," Mrs. Marsan approved.

"We've got a better one. *Union in Division.* In other words, the only way to keep civilization from disintegrating and mankind from mutual murder is to divide God's gifts equally so that men may be united in a common enjoyment of them." He stopped for breath, taking up his cup again.

"By the time all that dividing up was done people would be too played out to enjoy anything," Mrs. Marsan objected.

"I didn't expect you to understand," Mr. Cernak said coldly. "Your class is blinded by the glitter of gold."

"The Rhinegold. . . . Look out for the Nibelung . . ." Jessamine murmured. She began to hum.

Mrs. Marsan asked wearily, "What was the meeting today about?"

"Government ownership. Capitalist collectivism, operated for the private profit of the privileged as usual, as against the real thing."

"I want the real thing." Jessamine put aside her coffee with distaste.

"Genuine brotherhood," Mr. Cernak declared, "means the democratic control and operation of industry by the people who actually work it, and the sharing of the profits therefrom among the people who have earned them." He gathered force. "Not hogging and hoarding by a bunch of moneyed fatheads and bureaucrats!" His frail hand shook so that his cup rattled against the saucer.

"Moneyed fatheads!" Mrs. Marsan gasped.

"I wasn't being personal." He added righteously: "But large landholders are as bad as large factory owners."

She sighed. "I guess you mean the plantation. . . ."

"I hate it." Mr. Cernak moved uneasily in his chair. "I hate what it stands for."

"It don't belong to me."

"Your sister has it and it will belong to you some day. Besides, you're living off of it. That check you get every month—*you* don't work for it. *Others* do."

"That measly hundred and a quarter. I just about crawl along on it." Her eyes widened. "Mr. Cernak, you wouldn't want me to pick cotton in the fields, would you?"

"Cut that scene!" Jessamine raised her powerful white arms and began to swing them around like a windmill. "Cut that scene out entirely!"

"No." Mr. Cernak looked at Mrs. Marsan's hands that were plump and soft as dumplings and cleared his throat. A faint pink spread in his neck where the veins stood out.

"But I understand perfectly well what you mean." She smiled at him brightly. "Society is so unjust. Some folks have to work too hard. Like Mr. Ingalls, for instance. The only time he has for recreation is three o'clock in the morning."

"You don't say?" Mr. Cernak rested his cup.

"And Sundays, of course, being a holiday."

"Quiet young man. I never see him go out, except to the store."

"He don't have to. His recreation comes in taxis."

"You don't say!" Mr. Cernak repeated.

"The curtain went up on a lot of things last night." Mrs. Marsan selected a brownie.

"The curtain's gone up." Jessamine rose from her chair, and placing a large fair hand over the full-moon of her left breast began to sing the "Bell Song" from *Lakmé* in a soprano too big for the room. Lady, lying on the sofa beside Mrs. Marsan, threw back her head and howled.

"Well, he's young," Mr. Cernak said wistfully.

"Around twenty-eight, would you say?"

"Twenty-nine!" He had to shout to be heard above Jessamine and the dog.

Mrs. Marsan gave Lady pieces of cake to close her mouth.

"He told me so himself a few weeks ago," Mr. Cernak went on with less effort. "We were talking about Miss Larsch. He's quite an intelligent fellow, you know. Reads a lot."

Adrian Larsch was the high-school teacher in the third back, next to Mr. Ingalls and directly opposite Mrs. Marsan.

"He's certainly got women on the mind," Mrs. Marsan said.

"Well, he had Miss Larsch on the mind. I think he's in love with her."

"I don't. Not now."

Jessamine finished her aria and sat down.

"It's just as well. Miss Larsch won't look at him." Mr. Cernak leaned back in his chair and resumed his normal voice. "Maybe he's finding consolation."

"He's sure finding enough. They're making a week end of it. I sat up all night and she never did come out."

"Come out," Jessamine snarled. "Come out and curse the critics. . . ."

"Do you think she's still with him?" Mr. Cernak looked awed.

"I haven't seen her leaving. And I've been looking and listening all day."

"She might have gone since *we* came," Mr. Cernak suggested. "You haven't been watching the last half hour."

A light went out in Mrs. Marsan's face. She said "Oh" deflatedly and her mouth puckered into a pout. Then the light switched on again.

"I bet she's not gone," she said. "I'll bring them some coffee. They'll be glad to have a cup."

"I wouldn't do that!" Mr. Cernak started out of his chair

and the arm fell off. "A man doesn't like to be disturbed at such a time!"

"Nonsense," Mrs. Marsan said. "A man can eat at any time."

2

For an impatient minute it looked as if Mr. Ingalls would not be at home. Only technically, of course, for Mr. Ingalls had a hurried, heavy tread and if he had gone out Mrs. Marsan would have heard him passing by in the hall and thundering down the steps. It was the only time Mr. Ingalls ever advertised his existence. He went downstairs like a crate, thumping every step he did not miss.

She shelved the tray on her hip with her left hand and knocked again, a slow but insistent summons. There was a stir inside and the unhappy sound of a headlong body colliding with a corner. As Mr. Ingalls opened the door a crash came from the next room, as if a piece of the ceiling had fallen in.

He stood in the doorway tying the sash of his lounging robe, a faded blue and white stripe like mattress ticking. He was in pajamas. Mrs. Marsan's eyes lighted on his frayed slippers, fluttered up to his tousled hair. Mr. Ingalls was tall and blond. His hair was the color of the cornflakes that passed over his counter every day, and his eyes were a clear, intense, serious gray behind neat octagon glasses. He blushed easily.

"I thought you might like a little refreshment," Mrs. Marsan greeted him. "After working so hard," she explained, by way of excuse.

"That's awfully kind of you." Mr. Ingalls looked at the tray with its cozy arrangement of two's and the red in his face deepened. "I wasn't expecting—" His voice stuck and he glanced down at his peeping pajamas and slippers. "I *have* been busy," he said. "Did you hear anything? Did I disturb anybody?"

"Not at all," Mrs. Marsan assured him. "Drink that while it's hot. It will brace you up."

Mr. Ingalls took the tray from her. "Well, will—will you come in? The place is dreadfully upset." He looked embarrassed enough to die.

"No, thanks, I can't." Mrs. Marsan noticed his relief. "I have guests. You know—the Cernaks. You two have that tray together and don't worry about doing the dishes."

Mr. Ingalls was looking fascinatedly over Mrs. Marsan's head. She turned and saw Jessamine standing just outside her door, engaged in long sweeping bows to an invisible audience. "The performance is over," Jessamine announced. "Let's go home." She came swiftly toward Mrs. Marsan and Mr. Ingalls, and before either of them realized what she was doing, she swept past them into his apartment, jostling the tray so that some of the coffee spilled.

Mr. Cernak came.

"I'm so sorry," he apologized. "Jessamine is not herself."

"Oh, that's all right," Mr. Ingalls said.

"I'll get her out. It won't take a minute."

"She's entirely welcome." Mr. Ingalls was miserable but polite.

They went in after Jessamine.

She had sat down at a breakfast table set up in the middle of the living room, staring in bewilderment at the typewriter before her. She picked at a few keys, frowning. They made no more noise than the faint swishing of beans in a bag.

"Come, Jessie," Mr. Cernak said gently. "It's time to go to the theater."

"This cheap instrument is no good. It needs tuning," Jessamine scolded.

"You mustn't mind," Mrs. Marsan begged Mr. Ingalls.

Mr. Ingalls smiled and said he wasn't in the least sensitive; in fact, the machine didn't even belong to him—he rented it by the month. It was a silent and less likely to annoy the neighbors. He glanced at the wall which separated him from Miss Larsch when he expressed his concern for the neighbors.

Jessamine's eyes flared with remembrance. "To the theater!" she cried. She stood up so suddenly that the table teetered and the pile of papers on the end shuffled to the floor. All but Jessamine helped to pick them up. They were mimeographed price lists of vegetables and obsolete copies of changes in the point value of rationed goods. Mrs. Marsan's heart melted for Mr. Ingalls. Not even on Sundays, not even on *special* Sundays, was he free from the tyranny of other people's stomachs.

She straightened up and clapped her hand to her mouth. Jessamine had disappeared into the next room. That would be Mr. Ingalls' bedroom. The girl must be in there.

"Jessie!" Mr. Cernak called through the door. "Come on! The car is waiting!"

The sound of rushing water was the only answer.

"She's in the bathroom." Mr. Ingalls blushed. "Could she be taking a bath?"

"May I go see?" Mr. Cernak looked still more slight than he naturally was, as if he had shrunk from chagrin.

Mrs. Marsan thought Mr. Cernak might need help and started after him to offer it. Mr. Ingalls hovered unhappily in the rear. He asked indulgence for his housekeeping. The studio couch was unmade; the rumpled sheet and light blanket dripped over the side like soft icing on a cake and the foreleg had slipped from under so that the corner of the couch lopsidedly met the floor. Mr. Ingalls said he bumped into it hurrying to answer the door and the leg always came off when the couch was violently moved. Mrs. Marsan hardly listened to him. She was thinking of the bed of roses she had once seen in a film version of *Three Weeks* and never since forgotten.

"Edward Johnson is waiting for you to sign the contract, Jessie," Mr. Cernak was saying in the bathroom. "You'd better hurry or he'll go."

Jessamine came out, her incredible hair hanging down her back to her waist. She must have intended to wash it. Her lips trembled and she was flushed. "Hurry! Hurry!" she panted. She made a dash for the hall, Mr. Cernak after her.

"Well! Now we can have our coffee." Mr. Ingalls relaxed and changed completely. It was the first time Mrs. Marsan had ever seen him grin. It make him look younger and less serious.

It was obvious that the girl had gone. She could have been hiding in the kitchen, but it was unlikely. To make thoroughly sure, Mrs. Marsan looked in the closet when she went to warm over the coffee.

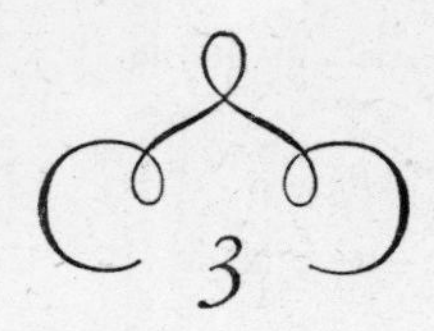

Sig told her the news. It was a sunny Monday morning and he was sitting in front of his stationery and soda shop in the scandalous porch chair which had no rockers, no arms, a broken back, and a raveled cane seat that hung in fringes. Miss Larsch was going to report the chair to Mr. Kennedy. She claimed it lowered the value of the property and the prestige of the tenants.

Mrs. Marsan always went down around eight to air Lady and get her morning paper. Faithfully she read the *Daily News.* She liked the love scrapes and the marriage tangles and the murders, skipping everything that pertained to politics or science. Best of all, she liked the pictures and the ads and the comics, and she read the Daily Horoscope the first thing, even before turning back into the building. The stars warned that the sun was in Scorpio, which was a time when people were apt to make mistakes, but promised that error would be righted in due course and the evening hours would be more serene than the morning. There was more about today being a good time for romance and making contacts, and bad for finances and domestic affairs, but before she could absorb it all Sig looked at her, blinking through his horn-rimmed specs, and said: "Did you know 4-F next to you's rented already?"

"Who to?"

"A widow." Sig got up and scooped the scattered pile of pennies off the newsstand into the pocket of his apron.

One of the pennies had a hole in it. "Doc," he muttered. "I give it to him yesterday."

"Has she got any children?" Mrs. Marsan asked.

"I only know she ain't got no husband." Sig was mad about the penny.

"When's she moving in?"

"Today," Sig said. "But her rent don't start till the first. That's Thursday."

"Who told you?"

"Kennedy phoned. I got to get the gas and light cut in right away. Everything got to be done, I got to do it."

"Well, that's what you're getting rent free for," Mrs. Marsan reminded him.

"*Who's* getting rent free!" Sig growled. "If I got to do everything, I'm paying my rent in blood and brawn."

"You better put some blood and brawn into that furnace," Mrs. Marsan suggested. "It's getting chilly."

She shivered and came inside. She would have to get her sweater out of the naphthalene and change the buttons on her heavy coat. For the last five years she had been moving them until now they were perilously near the edge. But she had better not bother about the coat today. She might miss seeing the furniture van unload. Mrs. Marsan found a fascination in other people's furniture. You could almost tell what they were thinking from the kind of furniture they had.

Half way up the stairs she had to stop for breath. She never had to do that coming down. Coral Sands passed her, a streak of gold lightning. "Marsie! I've got an audition!" And she was gone. That was Coral—always chasing chances.

At the top she almost bumped into Burt Villars. Though he seemed to be in a nervous rush, he stopped at the sight of her and stood there lighting a cigarette as if he had all the time in the world. He said good morning, touching his hat and looking at her from the side, in that way he had. He was going to be late for work. Maybe Vivien was sick again. Mrs. Marsan inquired about her. "She's all right," Burt said shortly, the cigarette in his mouth. He continued down the stairs, picking up speed as he reached the bottom.

Mrs. Marsan leaned over the balustrade and saw him flash through the door. Burt was tall and dark and wide-shouldered —the kind of man romantic women are always meeting in their minds. He wore a close-clipped mustache which Mrs. Marsan thought was gilding the lily. Burt was handsome enough without it.

After everybody went to work, only Jessamine was home— and Joey Brent. Mrs. Marsan must bring Joey the opera glasses right away. She was behind time this morning. Joey liked to have them early so she could see the white-collars getting on the bus for the Manhattan train at Bliss Street. If Mrs. Marsan hurried it might not be too late for the high-school crowd. The boys in their sloppy pants and checker-board shirts and the girls in dusters and sox with kerchiefs on their heads, giggling and squealing and hugging their books, delighted Joey more than the work rush. Three years ago she was one of them herself. And then there was the after-breakfast time when the neighborhood women walked their dogs. Joey knew all the dogs, their habits and dispositions, and gave them names of her own choice. Suds. Tidbit. Cloud. Mildew. . . .

Mrs. Marsan went in and got the opera glasses. She unharnessed Lady and called her to come along. Joey was crazy about Lady.

Unfortunately Edna was not, and thrice unfortunately Edna was home. Edna said dogs and cats were germ carriers. She objected particularly to Lady because Lady left cottony hairs on the rug.

"Thank you, I'll give Joey the glasses." Edna stood in the

doorway like a guard. She was dressed to go to her office, with her hat and coat on. "Pearl hasn't come yet and I can't leave Joey alone."

"I'll stay till she comes," Mrs. Marsan offered immediately.

Edna looked at Lady.

"No, thank you. I can afford to be late once a year, I guess." She was a stenographer-secretary with the American Express Company. She had been there for ten years—since she was eighteen.

Just then the bell rang and Joey's voice came from the kitchen: "I can reach the buzzer!"

They could hear Pearl loping up the stairs. She was a lanky negro girl with straightened hair that stuck out stiffly over her ears. Instead of a hat she wore an artificial pink rose with silvered leaves.

"Jeez, I'm late," Pearl panted.

"So am I," Edna Brent said, her lips pinched.

Pearl's bosom, already high in an uplift bra, rose belligerently.

"I got to get up at *nighttime* to get all the way from Harlem over here. Good thing I like traveling!"

"I've never heard you complain about that before—at *your* salary," Edna iced.

"No, but my sister got a baby last night—I mean the married one—and that never happen before neither!"

"I haven't time to discuss it," Edna said. She called good-by to Joey and grabbed her bag and left.

Mrs. Marsan and Lady and Pearl went in.

Every morning Mrs. Marsan brought Joey Mr. Cernak's opera glasses, and every evening Pearl brought them back to her before going home. They were valuable, inlaid with gold and mother-of-pearl, and dated from the time Jessamine was singing at La Scala Opera House in Milan, more than twenty years ago. Jessamine had presented them to her mother, dead a long time now. They had been used proudly on nights when Jessamine sang, so that not only were they worth money but Mr. Cernak treasured them for sentimental reasons. He had given them into Mrs. Marsan's keeping since Jessamine put them in with the garbage one day when she was not herself.

Since Mrs. Marsan initiated Joey into the endless delights of spying, the glasses were seldom idle. Joey and Edna had the corner apartment; that meant two windows facing Sixty-ninth and two on the other side. She wheeled herself from one window to the other, changing scenes. The buses and autos ran up and down Sixty-ninth, and there was the gas station, of course, across the street, and the hind end of the tavern, in the daytime tame as a snoozing cat. Sometimes the junk men passed in trucks, or, more exciting, in rickety old wagons drawn by shaggy horses, an arch of cowbells gangling and clanging over a load of newspapers and rags. Sometimes the fruit and vegetable men passed, splashes of color like markets out of the Arabian Nights. At noon and at three o'clock Donegan helped the kids over the street, standing out there grandly in the middle and holding up traffic with a white-gloved hand. Sometimes Joey heard the castanet clack of hoofs and wheeled over from the sidestreet window just in time to see a mounted policeman ride past. He looked like Sir Lancelot and Joey felt like the Lady of Shalott.

"Have you got the glasses?" Joey asked eagerly. She had on a red sweater and plaid skirt and looked pretty enough to put on a calendar. Her legs in the braces were thin, but the rest of her was plump and young and her short curly brown hair and larkspur blue eyes held lively glints. "Today's Monday. There'll be lots of wash to look at."

"More than wash," Mrs. Marsan said. "All kinds of stuff. Somebody's moving into the empty."

"Who? I hope they have babies and a bird!"

"One thing they going to have is roaches," Pearl said from the kitchen. "This building's buggy with them."

"Don't you kill any!" Joey called.

"I'm feeding them," Pearl chortled. "Jeez, if Miss Edna could see this."

"Serves her right," Mrs. Marsan said. "She could have something. Cat or a canary or *something*."

"Well, she bought me that swell radio."

"That's not alive." Big difference between lively things and *live* things.

"But who're the new people? When are they coming?"

"Any minute," Mrs. Marsan hoped. "Maybe now."

She went to the front window and looked out. There was no van at the curb, but the bus had drawn up at the corner opposite and a crowd was getting on. She saw Edna ahead in the jam, and Burt Villars and Coral at the tail end, lingering, stepping in last. There was something in the way he helped Coral up that struck Mrs. Marsan's eye with the impact of a cinder.

No wonder he was late. . . . Waiting to hear her go down, probably. Nicely planned accident, this boarding the bus together. Vivien better pull in the reins on Burt or he'd be running off the road. . . . Hard enough to hold a man *with* a marriage certificate. . . . You couldn't be sure . . . but those open-faced insurance company letters Mrs. Marsan saw every once in a while when she peeped in the Villars mailbox did look funny. . . . Vivien getting what must be the bills for her premiums addressed *Miss* Vivien *Fenner*—

Mrs. Marsan's reflections stopped abruptly. A slim girl in a tweed suit was coming into the building, her arms full of bags and bundles.

It was Mr. Ingalls' girl.

"Wait a minute," Mrs. Marsan said to Joey, starting across the room.

She reached the hall just in time to see the girl disappear into 4-F.

2

Burt and Coral were crammed in behind the farebox, unable to move, propped up by the people pressed around them.

He was looking at her in the round mirror above the windshield. Her brass-bright hair fell to her shoulders and rolled under; a soft brush of bangs lay over her forehead, a smooth margin between them and her sleek brown brows. She was cute, all right, he thought, but just a kid—couldn't be more than seventeen, eighteen. She must be doing all right. Dressed like it, anyhow. That leopard skin coat and that slice of a hat cost something—though he knew very little about women's clothes. Vivien paid for hers herself.

She caught him studying her and stuck out her tongue. His expression changed, and she turned her head and looked up at him and laughed.

"This is the first real chance I've had to look at you," he said. "Don't blame me for using it."

Coral squirmed around to face him and gave him the full benefit of her eyes. He saw that they were green, with dark pupils.

"Why, we've been seeing each other for months! Next door neighbors—we practically live together!"

"All I ever get is an evening glimpse of you in the hall." At every lunge of the bus he could feel her slim weight along the length of his body. "You leave rather late mornings, don't you?"

"It all depends. Sometimes the day's grief starts early,

like today." Coral's mouth drooped a little. "I've got my troubles. . . ."

"Mind telling grandpa about them?"

"Grandpa?"

"Me."

"Go on," she said. "You're not old."

"Twice as old as you, I'll bet."

"Thirty-six?" She searched his face with interest.

"Thirty-five," Burt admitted. "And my hair's still my own."

He could not help the reference to his hair. He knew it was good—thick and black, with a wave that he carefully kept from curl by attentive grooming. Her eyes went feeling above his ears. A pleased quiver lifted the corners of her lips.

"Come on," he urged. "Out with those troubles. . . ."

She told him about yesterday. From nine-thirty until noon she had waited around at the Martin Beck for her chance to spread her stock. Jerome Robbins was looking for girls who could sing and dance for the new Feigay-Smith musical. Tap and torch—just her line. But no soap. Something or other simply wasn't there. Experience, maybe.

"It's a long time since I've had a break." She sulked childishly. "Lots of busts lately, but no breaks. The only luck I've had for ages was winning a clock at Coney last summer."

He listened, frowning, to a long list of Coral's frustrations. He had no idea she was having such a rugged time. He wished he could do something for her. Damn shame. . . . The kid had class. She deserved to get somewhere.

The bus turned a corner and his arm stiffened instinctively to protect her from the crush of swerving bodies. He felt the slow stirring of a new sensation. He would have liked to hold the whole world off from her, to create a safe little private world for her himself. She was such a baby, for all her show of sophistication. She needed looking after. She could never make her way alone like Vivien. . . .

Things had been going better at first, she continued—probably beginner's luck. She'd done a short stretch of radio and a couple of out of town stands at Syracuse and Newark, then a lush engagement at a new club in the Village. But the club folded, leaving her out on a limb. That started her streak of bad fortune. When her funds burned low she took a job as elevator girl in a Fourteenth Street store for a while, long enough to buy her coat back from the girl she had sold it to and pay up some bills.

Burt let her talk, intent on getting the whole picture. She called off some of the stage shows and radio programs she had tried to make. . . .

"And there's always a hook to the bait that's put out for new talent. Half the time it's some has-beens fishing for pupils. In other words, they're looking for a job the same as me."

Jobs. . . . He thought with distaste of his own insignificant place behind the desk of a shabby downtown hotel. Perhaps he would hate it less if it enabled him to stand on his own, without Vivien's liberality. He was getting sick and tired of his dependence on Vivien. The fact that she tried to cover it up only made it worse.

"You're not listening," Coral complained.

"I *am* listening. I was just trying to figure out . . . You're in a tough game, but there ought to be some easier way to play it."

They were silent for a while. Burt was thinking hard. He was trying to hit on some advice, some way to help her, anybody he knew who might help. She sensed it and felt grateful and tender toward him.

"It's tough till you make it," she said. "I put in a full day's work just running around places. You ought to see the ads I answer."

"You know," the mention of ads struck a light, "I have an idea. It may not be a very good one, but it's an idea."

"Let's have it." Coral brightened.

"Have you ever tried modeling? It's good money, the hours are easy, and sometimes it leads to things in a big way."

"Think so?" Coral was interested.

"Well, I know of a case—" Vivien was talking about it a couple of weeks ago. A girl who modeled for Marie Louise three afternoons a week and for magazine illustrators off and on had made enough to take care of herself and her voice training and now she had gotten a place in a musical revue. He wished he had listened more carefully to the story when Vivien told it. "With something steady that didn't take up too much time, you could keep your head above water and go on with your singing and dancing until things came right."

"Sounds like what I'm looking for," Coral said thoughtfully. "But I'm not up on this model business. How do you go about it?"

"I don't know. But I'll find out—this evening. How about meeting me at the tavern for a drink and talk, about eight, say?"

Coral said okay, she had a nine o'clock date, but she could kill it. She no longer cared about this morning's audition, either. She'd rather be a model than a chorus girl at La Martinique. Maybe she'd just chalk it off and run down for a visit with her girl friend in the Village.

The bus came to a definite stop. The passengers began to push and shuffle. End of the line already.

"I thought we just got on," Burt said.

He considered asking her to go some place for a cup of coffee and a cigarette, but he was late enough as it was to have Seilers looking at him as if he had committed murder.

Anyway, there was still the long ride in to Manhattan . . . and tonight . . .

3

Vivien lay across the bed in a froth of chiffon and lace. The satin pajamas and fitted housecoats she formerly favored were folded away in tar paper in a closet. Stark colors like gold and green frightened her now. For negligées she clung to soft rose beige and blush, and loose, floating lines.

Burt looked in from the bathroom, sawing a towel across his back. His damp hair massed on his forehead in ebony rings.

"How about eats?" he said. "Got something good?"

"Pot roast and potatoes and peas." Vivien pressed her fingertips to her eyelids. "And there's a salad and some beer in the frigidaire."

"Fine." Burt swished the towel vigorously. "Nothing like a cold shower to start you starving."

"It's in the pressure cooker. You won't mind serving it up yourself, will you?"

"Not on the beam tonight?" He was busy drying his ears.

"I have a headache again. I don't believe I'll try anything to eat."

"Why don't you? Might be just what you need."

"I think I'd better not," Vivien resisted. When her head was like this the thought of food gagged her.

Burt threw the towel on the rack. It made a wet, stinging sound. He came into the bedroom, massaging his head.

"Listen, Viv. That Cinderella story you were telling me the other day. About the girl modeling for Marie Louise who got a part in a Broadway musical."

"Gloria," Vivien remembered promptly. "What about her?"

Burt stood before the full-length mirror, flexing his arms, making his biceps jump. Vivien, her head raised on the pillow, could see all of him—the square shoulders and muscled torso that tapered wedgewise to lean hips and thighs, the long legs and hard knot of the calf. He faced her from the mirror, chest covered with a dark down, stomach flat and firm. For a moment she hated him for not growing fat, for not getting flabby and lined and paunched. Except for a maturity of expression that made him even more attractive, he was as youthful as he was seven years ago. It was haunting, horrible that he should stay young while she grew old. Her temples throbbed like drums. At thirty-eight she could match him. Now she was forty-five. In the last year she could see herself going, like a bridge before a flood. Incredible that a single sudden year could work such changes. . . .

Vivien had not been listening to him. His irritation brought her back with a start.

"Well, for Christsake, don't you know? You seemed to know a mighty damn lot about it two weeks ago!"

"About what," Vivien said wearily.

"How she got going—how in hell she got to be a model—how she landed the Broadway business. Things like that don't just parachute from the blue—or do they?"

"For heaven's sake." Vivien raised herself on an elbow. Sick as she was, she had to smile at him. His thunder had an appealing helplessness, a touch of childish rage that always amused rather than angered her. "Anybody would think *you* wanted to be a model."

"I know somebody who does." Burt calmed down. "That's all."

He started to dress, slipping into his undershirt, mating button with buttonhole.

"She's got to more than want. She's got to work—I can tell

you that much. Work and worry and wait." Vivien considered him curiously. "Do I know the ambitious lady?"

Burt went to his bureau drawer for a shirt. He reached for a polo slipover and then changed his mind. He took out a favorite fresh from the laundry and slipped the supporting cardboard from the folds.

"Sure. It's that kid next door."

"That cheap little twist of tinsel?" Vivien's voice was hard. "She'll never make it."

"She can try, can't she? Hasn't she got as good a right to try as the next one?"

"I'm filing no objection—no objection at all. On the contrary, I wish her stacks of luck—she'll need it." Vivien settled back on her pillow, closed her eyes. Bright bubbles no bigger than pinheads rose out of the black.

"I bumped into her on the bus this morning," Burt said casually. "She was telling me about the rotten run she's been having and I told her about your friend to cheer her up."

"Did it cheer her up?"

He was snaking his belt through the tabs of his trousers. He looked over sharply at Vivien.

"You think it didn't?"

"I don't know. Except—when somebody's on the slump, telling her about another girl's success is sometimes clumsy comfort."

"I don't think she felt that way," Burt said tightly.

He went blindly around the bedroom, trying to think what he was looking for. "Slippers are in the closet," Vivien told him. Behind her closed lids, identifying all the little usual sounds, she could see him searching. Burt found his shoes where he had left them, in the bathroom. When Vivien opened her eyes she saw him fully dressed, hair pomaded into an undulating cap.

"Going some place?" She was surprised.

"Out of cigarettes. I'll step down for a minute after I eat." To the questioning arch of her brows he answered impatiently, "I'm just clean—that's all. Any crime in that?"

"You'd better go eat," Vivien said indulgently. "When you're hungry you're as pleasant as smallpox."

The sound of dishes and cutlery came from the kitchen, and presently the smell of food. Vivien turned her head aside. But when Burt failed to find the salad she got up and slipped on her mules and went to the frigidaire for it.

"Your eyesight's getting bad," she said playfully. And then she remembered with a twinge of nausea that the oculist told her she would have to wear glasses.

"Sit down, Viv."

"No, I'm going back to bed."

"You can stay out of bed a minute, can't you? I want to ask you something."

"Well, what is it." She leaned against the doorframe.

"I was thinking. Don't Marie Louise need somebody to take the place of the girl who's left?"

"Nobody could take Glo's place. She was the real thing."

"Marie Louise will have to get somebody, won't she?"

"I suppose so."

"Well, how about the kid next door?"

"Listen, Burt. Modeling isn't pushing pies across a counter. Gloria studied—hard—for I don't know how long. She studied at a school. It took money."

"Where did she get the money?"

Vivien shrugged.

"What school?"

"I don't know. There are dozens of them."

"I get it. You don't want to help."

"I'll find out the name of the school. I'll find out all about it tomorrow."

"Don't strain yourself." He got up from the table. "Forget it."

He went into the living room and picked up his hat and coat where he had thrown them on a chair. Vivien fled past him into the bathroom. She was going to be sick. She hoped he'd get out before it happened. She stood looking at herself in the bathroom mirror, holding her breath, heart choking her. His voice, too cool, came from the foyer.

"You won't even ask Marie Louise then?" Marie Louise knew Viv was good at thinking up women's clothes—she paid for Viv's cleverness with favors as well as a fancy monthly figure. Viv could make her take the kid on if she wanted to. . . .

"I can't ask her, Burt. She'd—" God, why didn't he go—"she'd think I was crazy."

The door slammed. The noise had the fury of an explosion. Even the walls seemed to rock. Vivien reached for the relief of being sick, but somehow the urgency had left her. The silence now was like a period to everything that had ever been before.

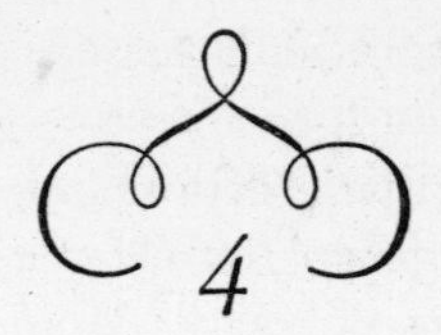

4

WHEN Mrs. Marsan, sitting at her window late the previous night, saw Burt and Coral coming across the street together, she put down Mr. Cernak's opera glasses and sighed. "You can't keep human beings from being human," she said to herself.

Mrs. Marsan often spoke to herself. It was a habit that had grown on her imperceptibly, like poison ivy climbing a tree, unnoticed until it was too strong to uproot. Not that she thought it poisonous or wished to break it. She had examined briefly the practice most people consider peculiar, the first time she realized it was there, and come to a quick and emphatic decision. A woman who lived alone, she concluded, should be on friendly terms with herself.

Only infrequently was the tone of the talk distinctly not friendly. On such occasions she conducted heated conversations, arguments, fusses, half aloud and half in her head, about things that nettled her. Blowing off her own top privately prevented her from blowing off somebody else's publicly.

A recent example in point was the matter of Edna Brent and the minister. If he wanted to come see Joey once every week and Edna was satisfied, nobody—not even Joey—could stop him. But nobody could stop Mrs. Marsan from telling herself what she thought of it. Church going to Joey since Joey couldn't go to church might be right, but was it reasonable? After the minister left, Joey always looked as if the actual church, down to the last bell and brick, had been brought in a sack and dumped on her.

Another thing that galled Mrs. Marsan was the way Adrian Larsch treated Mr. Ingalls. Adrian's arctic indifference was too infuriating to keep between Mrs. Marsan and herself. She drew Lady into the brawl, demanding from what cock-eyed corner of logic Adrian Larsch got her sense of super-importance. Between her and Mr. Ingalls, who was more necessary? When school was closed, who was sorry? But if groceries were closed, who'd be glad? You could do without learning but you couldn't do without eating. Could you? *Could you?* . . . Lady would look up at her out of eyes running rusty rivulets and yap sharply.

This afternoon Mrs. Marsan had a debate with herself and it looked as if her side lost.

What is Mr. Ingalls' girl doing in that empty apartment? I waited all day yesterday to see the van draw up and not so much as a wheelbarrow came. Three o'clock now and nothing yet. Not even sight nor sound of *her* today.

She must be across the hall in HIS *apartment. You're just wasting time standing here with your good ear to the wall. It's as quiet as mud next door.*

I saw the light under his door until after three again last night. If she's going to spend so much time in his place that she don't need furniture, why did she have the gas cut in? I saw the gasman come. I even heard him there, testing the stove, probably. What good is a stove without a pot?

You forgot. She can use Mr. Ingalls' pots.

Then why don't she use his stove? Maybe I should go see if she needs to borrow anything.

If she does, she'll ask. You'd better have a good cup of coffee and forget the whole thing. . . .

Mrs. Marsan went to the kitchen cabinet and took out a cup and saucer from the special occasion set. She hardly knew why, because she used it only on the Cernaks' Sunday afternoons. It was pale ivory banded in warm gold and decorated with a spray of field flowers. Mrs. Marsan had had it for years, ever since she came to live in New York after Henry died. Two or three of the pieces were chipped and the sugar bowl had lost an ear.

She poured herself a cup and put out a handful of cookies on a pink glass plate from the dime store. She cracked a cookie and threw a piece to Lady. "They'd taste better if I had somebody in," she said.

She looked in the cupboard to see if she had any of those gumdrops left that she got from Mr. Ingalls the last time she was at the A&P.

"The girl next door must be pretty lonely—in the daytime. I guess I ought to ask her."

What you ought to do is get that girl out of your head.

She poured the rest of the gumdrops from their cellophane bag onto another pink glass dish. Lady barked and received a gumdrop.

"New neighbor—it's my *duty* to ask her."

Mrs. Marsan felled the opposition triumphantly. The word duty was always an effective ax.

Never say you're beaten unless you say it with your last breath. She had won the debate after all.

2

The Charm Column in the newspaper stressed the importance of first impressions. They were lasting, it said, and special attention should be given to grooming and dress when initial meetings were to take place. How often valuable friendships were forfeited because first impressions were false—the Charm Column sighed—through some carelessness on our part that might easily have been averted!

Impatient as she was to knock on the door of 4-F, Mrs. Marsan was willing to concede a few minutes to grooming and dress. She remembered this morning's style hint: The gleam of gold on black is always a symbol of smartness. She wished she had something black and something gold to gleam on it. But Lady had been sick from eating ice cream in the lap of her only black crêpe and the spot had never come out. Mrs. Marsan admitted drearily that the trace of Lady's sickness was not the kind of gleam that would create the right first impression.

In the end she decided on her brown georgette hostess. As Jessamine said approvingly one day when she was herself, it put the accents on the right notes—hair and eyes—soft pedaling the hips and bust of the fuller figure.

Mrs. Marsan was sensible, not saddened, about her figure. At fifty-five she accepted her inability to get into a size sixteen as simple arithmetic, and was as resigned to it as she was to the multiplication table. More than resigned, she was relieved; for she could eat cream, cake and candy with the carefree enjoyment of a child, confident that an extra pound would spoil no contours, since she had none to spoil. If Nature, in making her only five feet tall, was determined to show more generosity when it came to width, there was no use quarreling with the scales about it.

As she stood before the mirror in her bedroom, patting the lace of the low neck into place, she was glad she had gone to Elvira's just the other day to have her hair done. Mrs. Marsan's hair was her most petted vanity. Every second week she went down to the beauty salon at the corner—under Joey and Edna—and had Elvira give her a wash, rinse, and set. It cost a dollar and a half but the investment yielded Mrs. Marsan vast dividends in elegance. At periodic intervals she had a henna pack and a permanent. Her hair had now acquired the color of tobacco, but she was well pleased. She wore it high on her head in an upsweep that relaxed into an all around pompadour, faultlessly corrugated by Elvira's expert art.

She reached for her powder puff and dusted her face and neck. Her nose was small and retroussé, but if it was neither strong nor well-shaped, like Jessamine's, it was, she thought with satisfaction, more sprightly. Thank heaven she had a full, fat neck instead of that stringy looseness which afflicted skinny women. A little rouge on each cheek made her eyes look brighter. They were brown, but the brown of black plush worn beyond its term. Yet they could sparkle. It was better than having unfaded brown eyes without a fizz in them.

Mrs. Marsan never spared herself a frank personal appraisal. Now. She looked nice. She had a good skin, smooth and fair. A second and larger edition of her chin joined her throat without curving, but she was free of the lines that scratched up thinner faces. Take on weight to take out wrinkles, she always said, and proved it.

A touch of perfume behind each ear completed Mrs. Marsan's grooming for the first impression.

3

The girl opened the door timidly. She was startled to see Mrs. Marsan.

"I—I thought it was the gasman back," she fumbled. "He couldn't get the pilot on the stove to work."

Mrs. Marsan was surprised herself. She had hardly expected an answer and was prepared to try Mr. Ingalls' door.

"I'm your nearest neighbor." She smiled. "I'll bet there's nothing wrong with that pilot. Can I take a look?"

The girl hesitated. Then she said, "Well, thank you. If it's not too much bother."

So there really wasn't any furniture. Never a sign or a stick. The newspaper carpet, put on the floor to prevent scratching when the bank had cleaned up and waxed after the last tenants moved, was still down. Otherwise the rooms, with the shades drawn, were as bald and lonely as caves.

There were a couple of empty cans on the kitchen sink and a cup with a sediment of tea leaves alongside a small pot which Mrs. Marsan recognized as local dime-store stock. A solitary roach ran along the tiled highway of the sink edge, detouring to investigate some bread crumbs.

"I've been using matches," the girl explained. "I really could do without the pilot, I guess."

"While you're paying rent," Mrs. Marsan removed the grate from over the gas burner, "you might as well get all the conveniences that're coming to you."

She peered at the pilot and sniffed.

"Choked up with grease. I'll bet all it needs is a good cleaning." She poked at it with a burnt match.

"Oh, don't," the girl begged. "You'll get your hands dirty. He'll be back."

"Well, what I really came over for—" Mrs. Marsan straightened. "Will you come and have a cup of coffee with me? It's all made, and I'm all alone."

"Well, I—"

"It's just next door."

"I'd better wait for the gasman."

"You'll hear him if he comes."

"Well—" She seemed uncomfortable.

"Come on," Mrs. Marsan urged. "We're going to live alongside. We might as well get to know each other."

"I don't want to know anyone." She stiffened and her lips thinned to a line.

"Come have a cup anyway," Mrs. Marsan insisted. "Since it's made."

The girl followed her out, as helpless as if she were hypnotized. "You can leave your latch off," Mrs. Marsan said. "It's so close." And you haven't anything to steal anyhow. . . .

After the nakedness of 4-F, Mrs. Marsan's living room with its faithful old art-square, floor lamp, chenille dot curtains, sofa and dilapidated chairs looked sumptuously cozy. The afternoon sun reached through the window, touching the bridge table laid out before the sofa and brightening the best set with a patina of that elusive quality which Mrs. Marsan included in the generic term *genteel.*

"Sit down," she invited. "That's Mr. Cernak's chair. You'll like Mr. Cernak. He wants to start a revolution." She went to the kitchen and came back with the tall gold-rimmed coffee urn filled from the agate dripper always on the stove. "It's good and hot. Let me pour you a cup."

The girl sat, stiff and silent, staring at the poodle. Lady stood before her wagging a sparse tail that fountained unexpectedly at the tip.

"Like dogs?" Mrs. Marsan chatted. "Her name is Lady. And that's what she is. She don't bite."

"*We* had a dog," the girl said dully. She drew away when Lady came near.

"Cream? Sugar—one or two?" Mrs. Marsan was glad there was some lump sugar left. She loved to use the tongs, though they were only nickel and black on the edges where the plate had worn off. "Next time you come I'll have some real cake." She passed the cookies, but the girl, sipping her coffee, ignored them.

"You just moved in yesterday, didn't you?" Mrs. Marsan settled back on the sofa with her cup and turned on a friendly beam.

"No. Saturday."

"Saturday?" Mrs. Marsan hiccuped.

"It was very late."

She passed the gumdrops but the girl refused. "Well,

maybe you'll feel like it later." She threw one to Lady. "I got them from Mr. Ingalls. He's such a nice young man, so serious." She paused. "Isn't he?"

"I don't know." The girl regarded her blankly. Her eyes were mist blue, like the agate dripper in the kitchen.

"He's your *friend,* ain't he?" Mrs. Marsan forgot to be careful about ain't.

"I have no friends in New York."

"Well!" Mrs. Marsan put down her cup. "Well, I declare!"

Silence rushed in like a draft. Only Lady, describing circles on the art-square in her struggle to get the gumdrop out of her teeth, made any sound.

"Here." You can't fool me, honey. You're hedging. "Let me fill that again. It must be cold."

The girl protested futilely. Mrs. Marsan filled her own cup too.

"Funny. . . ." Come now, dear. You don't have to be afraid of me. I don't mind young people being friendly. It's human and happy. "I thought you and Mr. Ingalls were well acquainted."

"I don't know him at all."

It sounded truthful. And if it was—

"For goodness' sake, then where've you been *sleeping?*"

The girl jerked her head at the floor, bit her lip and frowned. Mrs. Marsan jumped and her eyes leaned out of her face like a frog's.

"Really!—Weren't you *cold?*"

"No—the heat's on. I didn't mind."

Mrs. Marsan thought of something else.

"What did you *eat* all day Sunday! No gas—no electric!"

"I had some crackers and fruit in my grip. I wasn't hungry anyhow. Yesterday morning I went out and got some dishes and groceries."

If she had crackers and fruit in that overnight case, Mrs. Marsan calculated, she couldn't have had much else.

"Well now, as soon as your furniture and things come," she pumped gently, "you'll be getting settled. It won't take long."

"I'm not getting any things."

"But you'll have to have a place to sleep and sit and eat off of!" Mrs. Marsan had forgotten all about her coffee. It cooled untouched.

"I have to go now." The girl stood up determinedly. "Thank you for asking me in."

"You can stay a little longer, can't you?" Mrs. Marsan was so disappointed that for a moment she felt ill. "It's early yet!"

"I really must go." Her voice was as taut as wire.

Mrs. Marsan followed her into the hall.

"Imagine that! We haven't told each other's name yet. Mine is Lily Marsan—Mrs. Lily Marsan."

"I'm Jean Wilkes," the girl said. After a moment she added, "Landry. Jean Wilkes Landry."

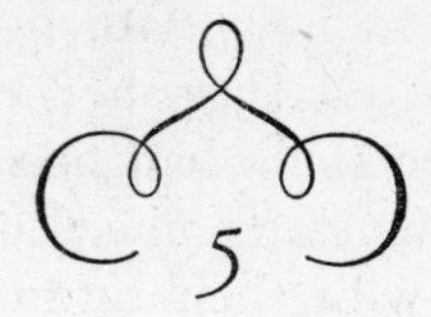

IT WAS Hallowe'en. Mr. Brinkmann's twins, impatient for dark, sat on the breadbox in front of his delicatessen producing ghoulish noises from under devil masks.

Everybody knew it was Hallowe'en except Adrian Larsch. She saw neither the devil faces nor the boys as she stepped off the bus and hurried across the street into the building and up the stairs. For her tonight was not All Hallows' Eve. It was Ballet Russe.

The door was barely closed behind her when she had the water running for her bath and a beaker of orange juice out from the frigidaire. While sipping the juice she looked at the desk calendar on the Hepplewhite adaptation that distinguished a corner of her living room. Some day Adrian Larsch would possess genuine Hepplewhite—or Sheraton—or Chippendale—or Duncan Phyfe. It did not matter which. All that mattered to Adrian was the ability to know them when she saw them.

Adrian Larsch taught Latin at high school. For five days a week she exacted the agony of conjugation and declension from writhing boys and girls, raveled out with grim patience the tough tapestries of Caesar and Cicero. All the time she was not teaching, she was learning. She rushed here and there, from lecture to exhibition to concert to opera, as if she lived in a constant vacuum which she was compelled to fill with activity. But it could be only one kind of activity. Cultural activity.

She was twenty-seven now, with no prospects—immediate—of marrying. It was not that she never had had any prospects; on the contrary, there had been beaux enough at college, and in the summers at home. But in the one case, they had been immature, with their futures too far ahead to see clearly; and in the other, they had no futures at all. Adrian had always known exactly what she wanted: she called them The Fine Gracious Things of Life, and in her mind the phrase flamed with illuminated capitals, like the handworked letters in medieval manuscripts.

One way to get The Fine Gracious Things of Life was to marry them. And one way to marry them was to prepare to marry them. Adrian had her plans laid and working. Lying awake at night she could see their ultimate dénouement. She knew she would never find anybody at school who would meet her measurements; the men on her faculty were grubs, wrapped in the cocoon of the classroom. Even with money—She tried to imagine one after the other of them passing from the chrysalis to the Purple Emperor of her plans, and the effort was futile and even fantastic. Sometimes, indeed, it was funny, and she lay back on her pillow and laughed out loud in the darkness. No, thank you. No high-school professor for Adrian Larsch.

A college professor—there, possibly, you had a different story. They traveled, they wrote books, they became well known, famous. They even became president—like Woodrow Wilson. Not that Adrian, for all her ambition, aspired to anything of that sort. The one thing she was not versing herself in was politics. Politics was not one of The Fine Gracious Things of Life.

She was not sure, after all, that being married to a college professor would be particularly profitable or satisfying. Those who ever left the campus were a freak minority, and the books they wrote were generally academic aches that languished in the shops. But men who wrote plays and novels—*success-fully*— Bits of newsprint nudged her eyes: "Gathering material for his new romance" . . . "in the Argentine, absorbing local color and gaucho background" . . . They traveled and bought pictures and made interesting collections, and in their social contacts skimmed the cream of cultivated, exciting people.

Something of the kind, Adrian thought, would be very much to her liking. And with her education and her cultural assets she could help her husband with what she used to catch him. "My dear, what was the second movement of that Beethoven 'Hammerklavier Sonata' we heard the other night?" . . . And Adrian would answer promptly, "The Scherzo, darling. *Assai vivace.*" She would be indispensable, irreplaceable, a wife and a well of wisdom all in one. . . .

To meet the Purple Emperor, Adrian would have to do a little preliminary traveling herself. This was part of the plan. For her purpose, boat travel was perhaps best. It was notoriously known that sea water cemented the most far-reaching relationships, that destiny prowled the decks of ships loaded with surprises.

Restrictions on travel were being lifted steadily, now that the war was over and the ocean lanes were opening up again. Just the other day she had read among the advertisements in the back of a magazine that advance bookings were being made to South American ports. Rio de Janeiro loomed alluringly on Adrian's summer horizon. She had cut the ad out and stowed it fondly in the mirror pocket of her purse. She meant to ask Edna Brent about it, to drop by the offices of the American Express herself for literature the first time she was in the neighborhood of midtown Fifth Avenue. The money was in the bank, a patient pile of systematic savings.

Meanwhile the important thing was to polish, to make of her mind a silver mirror and of her person a symbol of breeding and intelligence. Adrian did not want a man who was attracted by the physical first. Nor, in fact, second. The plan demanded a personality capable of recognizing in her at one and the same time the charm of both brain and body. Adrian did not have to strive hard to maintain a comeliness which matched the cool perfections of her mind. She was rather, to look at, like a piece of woodcarving: nicely turned, clean, stiff and hard in a way that lent her a sort of patrician dignity. She was not tall, but slim legs balanced on high heels, streamlined suits and the way she carried her pert head made her appear so; and the serene, steady gaze of her eyes—the color of steel—gave her a poise which was impressive, sometimes even a little frightening. Her most arresting feature was her hair, not because it was beautiful, but because it was odd. It was straight and the shade of hemp. Right now she combed it up in two sculptured wings flying away from the temples, with a tight braid leashing them across the crown of her head. The rather severe style was in a way a token of her fearless faith in herself. For her motto she had realistically chosen from *Hamlet: If it be not now, yet it will come; the readiness is all.*

The desk calendar held her attention until the orange juice was finished and the bathtub full. For weeks to come every leaf was inscribed with an engagement. Tonight Hurok's Ballet at the Metropolitan Opera House. Tomorrow at six-thirty her weekly class in Star Identification at the Hayden Planetarium. She must remember to buy Illyne's Star Chart and the Nautical Almanac. Friday, her evening session in Music Appreciation. Saturday at four, lecture at the Museum of Art: The Theory of Stage Setting from the Greeks to the Renaissance. Saturday night, concert at Carnegie Hall. Sunday matinée, City Center Opera. (Was it *La Traviata* or *Il Trovatore?*—she didn't remember. Well, she would bring the libretti of both. She would start reading them tonight—

English on one side, Italian on the other—while eating her dinner and later riding the train to town.) The dates ran their course, reminding her rigidly of the Philharmonic and Rodzinski, of recitals, of exhibitions, of foreign films, of more classes, more ballet, more lectures, more opera. And, oh, yes. She must get a ticket for *The Tempest* and read the play again before going. Her Shakespeare was tarnishing. . . .

Adrian left the calendar with its face open to tomorrow, the first of the new month. The black stick of the "one" jabbed at her memory. The rent . . . *Mon Dieu!*—for Adrian always exclaimed in French or Italian—with the fall season of this and that going full blast, she had been too busy to send her check. Well, she would make it out now and on her way down give it to Mrs. Marsan, who was always home, to hand to Mr. Kennedy when he came to collect in the morning.

And another thing. Before she forgot it she would sit down immediately and pen a note to the bank, owners of the property, and put it in with the check. That filthy freak which Sig Reiner persisted in using as a chair had simply got to be removed from the sidewalk. Words on the subject to Sig or to Hannah, his wife, were just so much water poured in a sieve.

Adrian reached into a drawer of the Chippendale adaptation and brought out a piece of thick white notepaper which she dated and addressed. "Gentlemen:" she began—her handwriting was strong and slanting, like heavy summer rain—"This is to advise—"

2

Mrs. Marsan and Mr. Ingalls were making a jack-o'-lantern for Joey. Mrs. Marsan had asked him this morning to bring a pumpkin and a couple of candles from the store and he himself, on delivering the bag, had offered to come in and carve out the face.

"The shell is pretty tough," he said. "You might hurt yourself. You need a good strong grip and a big hand."

Mrs. Marsan looked at his long hard fingers and then at her own, which were short and fat like baby bananas.

"Well, that's fine," she accepted eagerly. "Come right in. Wait. I'll get you the butcher knife."

"Let's do it in the kitchen," Mr. Ingalls suggested. "We've got to clean it, you know. It will make a mess."

They went into the kitchen and Mrs. Marsan put an apron around Mr. Ingalls. It went around him and lapped over largely on each side, since Mr. Ingalls had such a lean waist. She brought the strings to the front and Mr. Ingalls suffered her to tie a bowknot over his retiring stomach.

The pumpkin had a stem on it like a fox-terrier's tail. Mr. Ingalls neatly removed the top segment and scooped out the cobwebby insides and the seeds with his hand. "You learn how to do everything in the army," he said. Mrs. Marsan was not interested in the army but she was in Mr. Ingalls. She tweezed a few splintery facts out of him as he operated. His father had a farm in Nebraska. He was raised on the farm. He had been in the early fighting in Italy. He had been wounded. He had had an infection of the eye that was a worse nuisance than the wound. He was all right now. Everything was all right.

"How's that?" Mr. Ingalls had bored the eyes and scraped off a pair of brows arched like the back of a spitting cat. "Getting to look like something?"

"Fine," Mrs. Marsan said without looking. "Why didn't you go back to the farm?"

Mr. Ingalls said farming was not what he wanted to do. He concentrated on outlining with the tip of the knife a wedge that would subtract into a broad, flat nose. What he wanted to do, he added quickly, was not what he was doing, either, but it was something to do until he found out if he *could* do what he wanted to do. His tongue tangled in the confused words and he flushed. The wedge plumbed to the floor and Lady rushed to it, retreating after sniffing disdainfully.

"Does that look like a nose?"

"Couldn't be anything else.—What do you want to do?"

"Well, I—" Mr. Ingalls straightened. "I had a lot of time to read and think while I was in the hospital—Halloran, right over here on Staten Island. And one day I read something about Manuel Lisa. He was a fur trader, Spanish descent, the first white settler in Nebraska. Along around the beginning of the last century. Did you ever hear anything about Manuel Lisa?" Mr. Ingalls was flushed now with eagerness. His gray eyes lighted up his glasses like windows.

"Can't say I have." Mrs. Marsan raked her memory.

"He was really a remarkable man. He built Fort Lisa, the principal trading post of the plains region. He's called 'the founder of old Nebraska,' you know. A hard-working, hard-dreaming pioneer with the force of Niagara rushing through his veins and the strength of a storm!"

"My!" Mrs. Marsan had never seen Mr. Ingalls so enthusiastic before. She was vaguely aware that even in her apron with his hair falling on his forehead from leaning over the pumpkin he was a very nice-looking young man. He had something about him she struggled to name.

"I—" The red creeping up his neck returned to being embarrassment. "I'd like to build something, too—maybe." He went back to the pumpkin, sober and silent.

"Well, we all have our dreams," Mrs. Marsan sighed. She wondered what he wanted to build. "They don't cost a dime and they don't take up space."

"They cost time and they take courage," Mr. Ingalls said.

He worked absorbedly at fashioning a huge grinning mouth. He nicked square buck teeth from imagined ear to ear, then extracted three front side notches with a snip of the knife. The effect was hilarious. Mrs. Marsan laughed so hard that her stomach quaked and a tear squeezed out of the corner of her eye.

"You've got imagination all right," she applauded.

Mr. Ingalls stood back and studied his clown. He stepped forward again and lopped a saw edge out of the upper rim, slicing a gore in the forehead.

"That will give the candle air when the cap is on. And it's supposed to be hair—with a lock down the middle like Napoleon."

"It's the funniest thing I ever saw!" Mrs. Marsan screamed. "Oh, my God." She got a handkerchief out of her bosom and wiped her eyes. Lady jumped and yelped around her.

"Now for the dress rehearsal." Mr. Ingalls lit a candle and glued it into the lantern in its own grease. He put the tailed cap on. "The Basque beret," he said. The candle gasped for a moment, then caught its breath and brightly smiled.

"We'll turn out the light," Mrs. Marsan said delightedly. "Then we'll see—" She reached out and pulled the switch down to darkness.

For a full minute the kitchen rocked with sound. Lady looked at the fiery freak and howled unhappily through Mrs. Marsan's full-throated peals. Even Mr. Ingalls laughed. He had a good laugh—slow and friendly and deep.

"I knocked but no one heard me."

Adrian Larsch was standing in the kitchen doorway, gloves, coat and hat on, ready to go out. Her tone implied that nothing was expected to be heard above such a rowdy exhibition of noise. Mr. Ingalls quickly deposited his masterpiece on the sink. One moment more and he would have dropped it, creating a mess at Adrian's aristocratic feet.

Mrs. Marsan snapped on the light.

"My, you look swell. Going out?"

Adrian did not bother to answer a question the reply to which was obvious. She handed Mrs. Marsan the envelope.

"Will you give this to Mr. Kennedy for me when he comes tomorrow? It's the rent. I've been too busy to remember it. And I've written a note about that chair. I'm sure you'll agree with me that it should go."

"It's going," Mrs. Marsan said. "A few weeks more and Sig can sweep up the pieces."

"It's in pieces now. And I'm not going to wait a few weeks more for him to do the sweeping."

"It surely is an eyesore," Mr. Ingalls agreed vigorously.

"It's bad enough that the entrance has to be cluttered up with gum wrappers and sticky candy papers." Adrian shifted her opera book to the other arm. "But that chair has no excuse."

"Sig says he can't keep people from throwing the wrappers on the floor of the shop either. He says they buy a dime's worth of candy and they make a dollar's worth of dirt."

"I'm sure Mr. Ingalls exercises more discipline in *his* store," Adrian countered.

Mr. Ingalls remembered that he was wearing Mrs. Marsan's apron. He tried to unfasten it but the bow petrified into a stony knot. Adrian had the air of complimenting him but somehow he was unhappy; he did not feel complimented. He felt that he should make some modest acknowledgment but nothing coherent came.

"People don't eat things in Mr. Ingalls' store," Mrs. Marsan explained. "What they buy there they eat at home."

"They don't sit out in disgraceful furniture in front of his store, either. I'm sorry you approve of the chair," Adrian said shortly. "Anyway, please give Mr. Kennedy my note."

"*I* don't approve of the chair!" Mr. Ingalls assured her. "The chair won't be there when you come home tomorrow. You can depend on it, Miss Larsch."

"Well, Hannah can find some place else to sit and nurse Maxie, I guess." Mrs. Marsan shrugged.

"Some place more fitting than the sidewalk, I hope."

"She's weaning him anyhow. He would have been weaned already if she'd used quinine the way I told her instead of listening to Doc. Doc gave her licorice to make her tiddy black to scare Maxie, and instead of getting scared he liked it—licked it all up."

"Good night." Adrian was ice, while Mr. Ingalls brightly burned. "Excuse me for having interrupted." She turned to go.

"Miss Larsch!" Mr. Ingalls' panic snatched her back. "I have a book—*Philip II*—I'm sure you'd enjoy—"

"Thank you, but my reading schedule is full. Perhaps some other time."

"Well, if you ever—"

"I'll let you know." Adrian manufactured a gracious smile. "I must run now. I'll leave you with your lantern. As for me, I must go light my lamp." She paused significantly. "In all your reading, Mr. Ingalls, have you ever run across Browning? *The sin I impute to the frustrate ghost is the ungirt loin and the unlit lamp. . . .*"

Mrs. Marsan waited until Adrian's steps were on the stairs. Then she dug into the unsealed envelope and looked at the check and took out and read the note.

Mr. Ingalls was staring into space, his face stamped with humiliation and pain.

"She thinks—I'm satisfied to make jack-o'-lanterns," he said to the stove.

"Let her." Mrs. Marsan stuffed the note back into the envelope. "Not everybody could make a jack like that."

"It's from 'The Statue and the Bust.' And it's *each* frustrate ghost, not *the* frustrate ghost."

"Why didn't you tell her! How does it go? *I'll* tell her."

"Oh, no," Mr. Ingalls said hastily. "Just forget it. I must have heard her wrong."

3

On nights when Edna had to work, Pearl stayed with Joey until she came home. On such occasions Pearl collected overtime. Edna paid it grudgingly, because she allowed Pearl off from three to six every Wednesday to groom the Villars apartment, without subtracting anything from Pearl's pay, though Vivien paid her for the same time. Wednesday was the afternoon Pastor Frankel came to see Joey; and Pearl defended her position, and her wages, with the argument that as long as Edna wasn't paying the minister, there was no reason why she should discontinue paying her. "He's a visitor on these premises, isn't he?" Pearl had had six months at high school and flaunted it in a taste for fine words. "Do they dock the maid when there's a guest in the house? I have to leave tea ready for him, don't I? He's more work. I ought to get a raise." Pearl's logic exasperated Edna.

At five o'clock Elvira had left two customers under the dryers to come up and deliver a phone message. Edna had to work. She might be as late as midnight getting home.

When Mrs. Marsan brought over the jack-o'-lantern she found Pearl and Joey in the kitchen co-operating on the supper dishes. Pearl was at the sink, working with rubber gloves and a dish mop. Joey, in her chair, dried the pieces as Pearl handed them to her and stacked them on the oven top of the stove. When Pearl turned and saw the jack-o'-lantern she dropped a cup. It divided neatly on the floor into two symmetric halves.

Joey wheeled around and took the pumpkin in her lap. "What a beaut!" She leaned back and admired it all around. "Who made it?"

"Mr. Ingalls. He likes to make things. He wants to build something."

"Bridges?" Joey was warm with excitement.

"Maybe he could build a roach cage." Pearl laid out a few more scraps along the back of the sink. "They'd be easier to feed that way and they wouldn't be crawling all over the place. You ought to see them over at the Villars'."

"You ought to see them at my place," Mrs. Marsan said. "Kitchen looks like Coney Island on a Sunday in July."

Joey laughed.

"They're lots of company. And fun—you have no idea. Look at them now. Dancing the reel!"

"Wait till Lady has puppies. I'll give you one," Mrs. Marsan promised.

They all looked at Lady, sniffing around the stove.

"I've been thinking of Doc Kincaid's Scotch terrier."

"You mean Lord Dundee?"

"You mean Lord, Miss Edna!" Pearl rolled her eyes.

"I'm going to speak to Doc about it. Maybe tomorrow. He might be persnickety because his dog's got a pedigree and Lady hasn't."

"Maybe the new neighbor has a dog?" Joey asked hopefully.

"Oh, her. She's hardly got a pot."

"You *know* her already?"

"I had her over yesterday. They won't own up to it, but I think her and Mr. Ingalls are—friendly."

Pearl whistled softly. "What do you know!" Joey looked at the pumpkin, still on her lap, and said disappointedly: "Then she won't have time to be lonesome."

"They the kind that get lonesome," Pearl stated. "Unless they got work. You take my sister Bella—since she quit her job and took up with Alfred she so lonesome she near gone crazy. They ought to keep on working—like Miss Vivien and Mr. Burt."

"What?" Mrs. Marsan was not sure she had registered the right idea.

"*They* not married," Pearl tossed off. "They got all the symptoms."

"What are the symptoms?" Joey asked eagerly.

"Satin—satin's one of the first symptoms. The way she's got that bedroom fixed up—it's grand as a coffin. And the bed—it's all satin too, and it hasn't got a foot. All respectable married beds have got a foot. You take my sister Edie—she's the one got the baby. She married and her bed has got a foot. But not Bella's."

Mrs. Marsan listened raptly.

"Are there," Joey breathed, "any more symptoms?"

"Mirrors. Everywhere you look she got a mirror."

"Why, it's—*wonderful!*"

"That's what I think." Pearl studied her enameled fingernails to ascertain the extent of the day's damage. "Me, I don't want to get married. I want to be took up. Maybe I'll keep on working and maybe I won't. I'm different. I can be a lady without getting lonesome."

"No." Joey sighed. "I'm the type that would get lonesome. I want to get married and have a baby like Edie. I love satin. . . ." She sighed again. "But I guess I could do with a respectable foot and a candlewick spread."

There was a drumming on the door. Pearl said "Jeez" and her hand swept out toward the scraps.

"Wait a minute." Joey stopped her. "It *couldn't* be Edna."

It was Coral Sands. She was going to a party. She had on a sea-green net dress with blinking silver sequins caught in the folds; they spangled like stars reflected in a calm evening ocean. Her brass hair hung to her bare white shoulders. A chain of stars circled her neck.

Joey shrieked, "Co, it's *gorgeous!*" and Pearl stooped and counted how many layers there were to the skirt. Mrs. Marsan said, "Must've cost you a pretty penny."

"It's a present," Coral beamed. "Knew you'd like it." She pirouetted on silver pumps. "Good God." Her eyes widened at the pumpkin. "What's that you're nursing!"

"We better get out of here," Pearl said. "Kitchen's not right for a dress like that."

She wheeled Joey into the living room, to her place next the front window. Mrs. Marsan put the lantern in the middle of the table.

"I'll bring you all the favors I get at the club tonight, to keep him company." Coral stood admiring the pumpkin. Together they looked like a magazine picture of Hallowe'en.

"Don't get drunk and lose them, Co." Joey remembered the last time.

"This is a very dignified date," Coral asserted. "It's really more like a business engagement. He's going to introduce me to a man who's looking for showgirls and dancers for a club in Havana. If I'm lucky I'll be lolling in the sunny sands of Cuba this winter, kids!"

"We'll keep our fingers crossed," Joey said.

"He's sending a taxi for me. I have to get my coat and bag." Coral was never so beautiful. "So long. I have to run!" She vanished, leaving a whisper of expensive perfume in the air.

Mrs. Marsan stayed till the taxi came and from the window they watched Coral get in and ride away.

On her way to her apartment a half hour later she passed Burt and Vivien in the hall. Vivien was dressed in rich black, a red flower in her dark upswept hair. The flower had a defiant air, which Vivien herself did not share. She looked tired, readier for bed than for going out, her eyes so deeply ringed that they seemed bruised. Burt stopped to light a cigarette. The flame threw a little flashlight in his face. He, too, looked tired.

Mrs. Marsan could not quite explain it. Burt's was not a physical weariness, like Vivien's.

4

Mr. Cernak came over to borrow a dose of aromatic spirits for Jessamine. It was nearly midnight and Doc had the drugstore closed and in darkness. Mrs. Marsan could not sleep—thank goodness. She had been sitting in her box seat at the window, Lady on her lap, a cup of coffee on the window sill, since nine o'clock. Long ago she had lost count of the cars behind the tavern; she saw the couples getting out, arms around each other, drawn to the magnet. Nick Dinapolis must be making money. All that talk about closing up and going to Florida was just that—*talk*.

The tavern was not the only excitement. Since early dark the kids had been out in costume—cowboys, gypsies, in stuff rooted out of cellars and attics. Elvira's Angelo and Hannah's Ruthie had a fight, which Hannah and Elvira, rushing to their aid, made louder and longer. Hannah yelled in Polish, Elvira screamed in Italian, and miraculously they understood each other. Mr. Brinkmann came out from his delicatessen and settled it in German.

Now all the younger kids were out of sight and in bed. The street was cleared of little girls dressed like old ladies and boys in their sisters' skirts and high heels. The squealing and bawling was over, and doorbells were at rest. The big fun was beginning. The teen-age terror roamed the neighborhood. They swarmed the block, disappeared, swarmed back again.

There were seventeen to twenty of them, high-school boys in mackinaws and loud checked shirts with the tails out, noisy and rough. Donegan was off duty since school-out and they had a free field. Once the police car cruised by just after the boys had stoned the street lamp. There was not a boy in sight.

Mrs. Marsan was sipping her coffee, waiting for the next act, when she heard the quiet rap that could only be Mr. Cernak's. She slipped her kimono over her flannelette pajamas and passed the powder puff over her face.

"It's Jessamine's nerves again," Mr. Cernak explained.

In less than a moment Mrs. Marsan grasped the situation. It was the last of the month and Jessamine must have reached the last of her allowance yesterday, perhaps the day before. Mr. Cernak had a standing agreement with Nick at the tavern that Jessamine could have fifty dollars a month credit. If she used it up in a week, it was up to her, but after that she could have no more. Jessamine accepted the arrangement with a strictly honorable adherence to the rules. If, as usually happened, she fell short of credit two or three days before the first, she did not heckle Nick, she did not pester Mr. Cernak for one extra penny. Grimly she counted the hours until the calendar flashed on the green signal "Go!"

"She's been reading her notices all day," Mr. Cernak worried. "Sometimes I think if she'd just consent to burn all her scrapbooks, she might get better."

"Why don't you talk to her about it. Some time when she's sober. Like now."

"She's too nervous now." Mr. Cernak's Adam's apple jerked uneasily. "The truth is—I hate to see her past destroyed. It's bad enough her future was."

Mrs. Marsan went to the bathroom and returned with the bottle.

"I'll bring it right back."

"Don't bother. Keep it until tomorrow."

"No. I'd better. You might need it." Mr. Cernak's solicitude for Jessamine overflowed onto Mrs. Marsan. "You don't think enough of your heart."

"Pooh." She waved a hand. "Other things are more interesting."

Mr. Cernak disappeared into the apartment on the other side of the stairs and Mrs. Marsan stood for a few minutes in the hall, looking at the late ray of light barring Mr. Ingalls' sill. A sound of shouting, mingled with Sig's swearing and the din of metal on pavement, hurried her in to the living room window.

The boys had emptied onto the curb the twelve cans of ashes which Sig put out earlier in the evening for the morning pick-up. Now they were kicking the cans down the street. The noise had gotten Sig out of bed; there was a light in his store that flowed out onto the sidewalk and showed up the ashes, scattered like snow. Duffy was the leader of the gang. Mrs. Marsan saw him come out of Sig's with the chair the whole neighborhood knew. He dashed over to the gas station with it, followed by his mob. Fascinated, Mrs. Marsan watched what they were doing. They unhooked the hose, drained it of remnant gasoline on the ground; then they set a match to it. The flames licked the pavement, blue at first, then leaping red. In the heart of it the chair burned and crackled.

The boys had discovered the desperate adventure of draining the hose and firing the gas. They repeated it with the other three pumps, and presently the paved triangle in front of the gas station was a bonfire. The excitement was too great to allow for noticing the gray precinct car which had just coasted around the corner.

They were caught at last. The police—five of them—jumped out of the car and closed the trap. The flames shrank, snaked along the ground and out of sight, while the law took names and addresses and handed out ominous white papers.

Mrs. Marsan was so absorbed that she had not noticed Mr. Cernak's return with the medicine. She was aware of him standing next to her at the window only when he spoke.

"That's a shame!" Mr. Cernak protested. "An insufferable shame! They'll make criminals out of those innocent boys!"

"They could overlook their devilment *one* night in the year," Mrs. Marsan seconded. "Let them have their fun. They'll be over it soon enough."

"That's what we're paying taxes for." Mr. Cernak was excited. "So the State can maintain police forces to protect the property of *the few*, curtailing the liberties of the many. So the State can be an armed power over the people, using the police as the big stick of the ruling class to beat the ruled class into subjection!"

Mrs. Marsan understood Mr. Cernak only vaguely. She wondered aloud if all the boys would be taken to jail in the Black Maria, or if their parents would be notified to bring them to court, like the last time, when they dropped lit cigarettes in the mailboxes.

"They won't be run in—not if *I* can help it!" Mr. Cernak's voice trembled. To Mrs. Marsan's amazement he fled from the room down into the street.

She opened the window and held her good ear out to catch what was being said. The loud talking was so tangled and thick that it was difficult to follow. Over it all the big policeman bellowed: "These gangsters are destroying private property and one way or the other they're going to pay for it! And if *you* don't like it, it's just too bad." Mr. Cernak screamed; it must have been Mr. Cernak because the words were his, though the voice only faintly resembled him: "*I don't believe in private property!*"

There was a dead silence, while unanimous attention was

directed on Mr. Cernak. He looked even more slight before the large man in uniform.

"So you don't, don't you?" The big voice drawled unpleasantly. "*You* wouldn't be the guy who paid these hoodlums to bust up things, now, would you?"

Duffy blubbered something and the other boys chimed in. For a full minute it was impossible to get a word out of the confusion. When it subsided the big voice boomed again. "Well, maybe we'd better make a date with you, too."

He took Mr. Cernak's name and handed him a slip of paper.

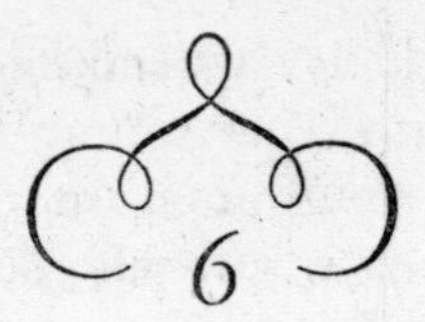

6

JEAN LANDRY had slept badly. It was not the floor, which left a knife in her back, and the stinging numbness in her arm from serving as pillow. It was the noise. Two o'clock came and went by her wrist watch before the neighborhood grew reasonably quiet.

After that it was the noise in her head—things remembered running in circles and sometimes colliding against reality with a sickening crash. This month three years ago—this month two years ago—this month last year—this month now. . . . It was always autumn. There had never been a spring.

The first autumn was the beginning, and the third the end.

She remembered her costume. It had been yellow sateen with black net flounces from hip to hem. It had a sateen bodice with a low heart-shaped neck and an impossibly huge red rose caught on one shoulder. The party was at Julie Kern's. Julie said, "This is my cousin Greg—the one I've been telling you about." They danced, and Greg told her about studying engineering at Northwestern and places in The Loop and how cold it was driving along Lake Michigan in winter. Later they ducked in the same tub for apples and melted lead and looked in mirrors lighted with candles. It was the best party Jean had ever been to in Bethany.

The following summer Greg finished his course and in October they were married. Greg was in uniform. They stayed on a few days in Chicago, until Greg got his orders.

The house in Tampa haunted her most. It was as close to

MacDill Field, where Greg was training, as they could get it. Not much of a house—living room, bedroom, kitchen and bath—but they had everything in it. Even a canary and a fox-terrier—Pete—with one knuckle of tail and a perennial black eye. There was a porch, and a porch swing. Roses bloomed in the frontyard in November, and for Christmas all the snow they had was moonlight on the whitewashed picket fence.

Greg was sent overseas the first week in January. She stayed on in the house, holding fast to the scant three months they had had together. The canary sang and the roses were as red as ever and Pete yapped and jumped when anybody came up the walk. Everything was so much the same, she could make believe, sometimes, that Greg was no farther away than the Field—that he might be coming up the walk at any minute. The house was full of reminders, and she reveled in them, keeping them alive and warm with her presence.

She stayed until the telegram came, this month a year ago—the third autumn. After that the house, which could never before be full enough, was too full of yesterday. At every move and turn she bumped into angles sharp with meaning. It was difficult if not impossible to get transportation for her household effects and she disposed of them, numb and blind, without daring to watch them go. Afterward, she could never forget sitting in the bare kitchen, looking at the money in her lap. It was cold and dry, like dead leaves.

She found homes for Pete and the canary and went back to her sister in Bethany. Nora had just had her second baby. Her husband was in the Philippines.

Nora meant well. She spoke continually of things like Social Security and Insurance and Gratuity and Pension. She had always been the practical one. To Jean every word of it was a drop of acid in the gash. There were times when she hated Nora, and hated herself for hating her. Nora was good, if tactless and clumsy. Jean gave her the important documents, screaming silently with pain; she had wished to keep them put away at the back of the bureau drawer which she never used. The marriage record, her birth certificate, the letter of confirmation of the War Department telegram. Nora filled out forms, asking her necessary questions that nailed Jean to a cross of recollection. Nora gave her papers to sign, dragged her out to a notary public.

Jean was glad there was no Social Security; the money would have galled her. The service insurance went to Greg's mother, as Jean had wanted it to at the time Greg told her he was taking it out in favor of both of them; again she was glad. But Nora saw that the six months' gratuity was realized and put in the bank in Jean's name. Jean refused to sign any more forms, put in any more claims. The idea of a pension check coming monthly to shout at her that Greg was dead threw her into deep hidden currents of panic which Nora could not guess from Jean's surface calm.

When the package came from the Army Effects Bureau she took it quietly to her room and waited until late at night to open it. It was a damp, mud-soaked carton—handkerchiefs, underwear, socks, the pen and pencil set she gave him that last Christmas, the picture of her he had carried in his wallet. She took the things out and shrouded them in a pillow slip, folding over the ends into a neat bundle and laying it on the topmost shelf of her closet, tenderly, as if it were something still alive.

On Christmas morning there was the letter from the chaplain, but she did not read it until several weeks later. By then she had the scroll signed by the President, carefully mailed in a cardboard cylinder. She looked at it a long time; the name seemed unfamiliar and almost foreign in Old English type on white parchment. In grateful memory of Lieutenant Gregory James Landry, who died in the service of his country. . . .

The chaplain's letter and the memorial she took with her when she made her delayed trip in the spring to visit Greg's mother in Chicago.

Every day and every duty chipped off another piece of her somewhere inside. The agony lay in her chest, hard and heavy. She had to carry it with her wherever she went, whatever she was doing. Often it would not let her eat or sleep, choking her, holding her eyes wide open to the blank ceiling. Sometimes she tried to cry, letting the sobs come up like sickness, but no tears came; the hard heaviness was there behind her eyes, blocking the way.

She helped with the household, hearing Nora's instructions through a fog. "Run down to the butcher and see what you can do, will you?" . . . "Think it would be absolutely brazen to borrow a cup of sugar from next door?" She felt that Nora wanted to get her out into the air, make her talk to people, and she always went. Everybody was kind, without suspecting that the sincerest sympathy is sometimes the most refined cruelty.

People hurt, but things hurt still more. She tried not to look at Nora's canary, she wanted to stop her ears to his singing. V-mail in the letterbox. The neighbors' porch swing. A briar pipe in the drugstore window. Red roses with Bethany's springtime. Julie Kern's house. . . . After a while, not only these, but everything—tables, chairs, beds, dishes—became a source of some likeness to sting the memory. Even smells and sounds were enemies. Biscuits baking. The laundry scent of fresh sheets. Sunday morning coffee. The bark of a terrier in the street, or the sudden gust from the radio of some song they both used to like. The babies—everything about the babies.

Jean said nothing to Nora, or anybody, about the way she felt. Her grief was all she had left now, and she wanted it to herself. She never spoke of Greg; she tried not to think. But she dreamed of him nearly every night, waking incredulously to a dark without him, unable to sleep again.

Then summer came, and the church bells rang and the firehouse siren wailed and people went mad and said the war was over—as if a war could ever be over, for the living. And two weeks ago Nora's husband came home.

Jean was not sure what she was doing, not even when she drew the five hundred dollars out of the bank. She only knew she wanted to escape. People and things were crowding in on her, giving her no quarter to breathe. One way to get away from people was to be lost among them, to be an indistinguishable pinpoint of sand among millions of shifting grains. To get away from things was harder. . . .

She drank her tea and ate her roll from the top of the kitchen stove. It was the last roll and the last of the canned milk. She would have to go out sometime this morning for food. She would have to think of getting a coat, too, now that November had come. A plain cloth coat, as unlike as possible from the fur beauty Greg had given her for a wedding present, before they knew they would be wintering in Florida.

The circle was complete again. No matter how it started out, it always curved to a finish at the house in Tampa. . . .

2

If Jean had seen Mrs. Marsan at the vegetable stand behind the canned goods, she would have walked around the block until she was sure the zone was cleared. As it was, she found her only after making the tour of the cereals and turning the corner to the juices.

Mrs. Marsan said hello happily. Sensing that Jean was in a hurry to get away, she dropped the cabbage she was weighing. Then she saw there was a sufficient line at Mr. Ingalls' counter to hold Jean up for a while, and calculatedly bought spinach, which she hated, and celery and kale, to make three bagfuls. She carted it all up directly behind Jean.

"I'm in such a rush," she said. "And look at that line, and me last. Wouldn't that kill you?"

"You can get ahead of me if you want to," Jean offered. She had very little, but she would feel relieved to see Mrs. Marsan out of the place and away.

"Well, every minute helps, don't it?" Mrs. Marsan pushed forward. "I sure do appreciate it."

This was going to be a double-header in excitement. Friday was her shopping day, on account of special week-end prices, but she had come this morning expressly to tell Mr. Ingalls the news. It was likewise the first time she had him and Jean Landry together, and she told herself that once and for all she was going to find out whether one and one made two or zero.

Mr. Ingalls was visibly upset to hear about the boys and Mr. Cernak being summoned. He wanted to know all the details and Mrs. Marsan gave them. Mr. Cernak had to appear at three o'clock this afternoon, and Donegan, who got the whole story from Sig, said he might be charged with contributing to juvenile delinquency or aiding in the destruction of property or both. The boys were booked with malicious mischief and Sig had entered an additional charge of theft against them for the chair. Sig wanted ten dollars' damages for the chair, which, Miss Larsch would be glad to hear, was damaged clear out of existence. It was a neatly put up job, Mrs. Marsan explained, the way the boys created a racket on the sidewalk with the ashcans so Sig would come out and they could get in and steal the chair, though why in the world they had set their minds on that piece of trash was a mystery except that it seemed somebody had paid them to do away with it.

"And the police think it's Mr. Cernak," Mrs. Marsan finished, out of breath.

"Nobody paid them," Mr. Ingalls said, annoyed. "I merely told Duffy I'd give five dollars to get the thing out of the way, that's all."

He was so disturbed that he ground Mrs. Marsan's coffee for percolating instead of drip and had to do another bag. The odor from the machine was sweeter than incense.

"He sure did an honest job of it," Mrs. Marsan reported. "You get your five dollars' worth. Not even the ashes're left. Wind blew them away."

A few more customers had come up behind Jean and the set of Mr. Ingalls' face indicated that he was not inclined to further discussion. Mrs. Marsan let the matter rest. She had found out enough to satisfy her. As Mr. Ingalls put her purchases in her bag he asked with concern, "Do you know when Donegan goes to lunch?" He went around one-thirty, after seeing the school children back across the street for the afternoon session. Mr. Ingalls seemed somewhat relieved. "I'll see him in my lunch hour," he said.

Jean moved up and Mr. Ingalls checked her few cans and cartons on the adding machine and put them in a bag. Mrs. Marsan fiddled with her load and watched them expertly. *Either they're the smartest couple ever created, or he don't know her from a sack of salt.* Absolutely no symptoms. Never a shred of satin in their looks, both of them as wooden as a bed with a foot.

Mrs. Marsan wrote a disappointed No to the question which had teased her fancy for days. She had hoped Mr. Ingalls was finding happiness, a little of his own best jam for the dry slice of his humdrum daily bread. Now she knew Mr. Cernak was right; he was gone on Adrian Larsch. No matter what he expected, he was lucky if he got so much as a crumb from that quarter.

Jean picked up her bag.

"I don't know how in the world I'm going to get all this home," Mrs. Marsan fussed. Then she smiled. "Aren't you lucky to have just one."

She could see that Jean was struggling between the desire to run and the necessity of being civil.

"Maybe I could carry some for you," Jean said helplessly. "Are you sure you wouldn't mind?"

Mrs. Marsan gave her the spinach. The girl looked as if she could barely carry anything heavier. There was something still funnier about her—since it wasn't Mr. Ingalls—and Mrs. Marsan wanted to know what it was.

3

Hannah was nursing Maxie on the sidewalk in a new chair. Mrs. Marsan called it new in the first shock of surprise. Actually it might have been older than the other. What she should have said was, a *different* chair. It was an overstuffed, faded and stained, its worn skin bursting in spots to ooze dirty tufts of cotton.

Miss Larsch would like this even less. The rockerless rocker had at least been clean. Mrs. Marsan ached when she thought how little Adrian Larsch would thank Mr. Ingalls for all his trouble. She regretted having destroyed the note before handing Mr. Kennedy Adrian's rent when he collected this morning. Why worry Mr. Kennedy for nothing, she had argued. He had enough leaky faucets and broken window sashes to think about without wondering what to do about a chair that was extinct anyway. Now a substantial ghost had risen to take its place and to confront Mrs. Marsan accusingly.

If Adrian ever asked anything about the note, Mrs. Marsan would say it must have dropped out and gotten lost. The envelope wasn't sealed, was it? Mrs. Marsan approved of lying. It made life easier for everybody. And anything that made life easier was not a sin. It was a social duty.

She was thinking so fast as she climbed the stairs that she forgot to rest midway as the doctor instructed. Besides, the bags added an extra burden to her weight. Jean Landry followed quietly, without saying a word. At the top of the stairs Mrs. Marsan had to lean against the wall and suck for breath. Her heart was bouncing like a ball.

It was Jean who opened the door and carried the purchases in to the kitchen. Lady came to meet them, giddy with welcome.

"That's a help." The scheme was panning out perfectly. "Stay for lunch, won't you?"

Jean looked panic-stricken.

"Of course you will," Mrs. Marsan urged. "We can have a cheese omelette and some salad. And do you like peaches and cream? And the coffee's fresh ground."

"I'm sorry. I can't stay." Jean hugged her bag as if she wanted to hide behind it.

"I only thought—I'm not feeling well. And if you *could* stay—I hate to be alone when I get these attacks." Right now I'm feeling fine and if that little nip is the worst bite I ever get I'll be lucky. But I have to find out about this girl.

Jean hesitated uncomfortably.

"I have to sit down." Mrs. Marsan took a chair at the breakfast table. "Sit down a minute too. Then if you don't want to stay for lunch you can go. It's only eleven-thirty," looking at the wall clock.

For a while they sat in silence, watching Lady chase a roach.

"I can't put anything down for them on account of the dog," Mrs. Marsan explained when Lady had caught and eaten it. "Once she ate a lot of poisoned ones and nearly died. I guess you're troubled, too, Miss Landry? Is it Miss or Mrs.?"

"It's—Mrs."

"Husband still overseas, I guess?"

"He won't come back." Jean looked at her hands, tight-clasped in her lap.

"Oh." Sig had it right then. A widow. It was a queer world where young girls like this could be widows. "Happen a long time ago?"

"A year."

She don't want to talk about it, Mrs. Marsan thought. Some women were like that—they locked a thing up in their hearts and were fools enough to think they got rid of it that way. You couldn't do that with grief. You had to double up your fists and face it.

"Must have found it pretty hard to find an apartment in New York right now, didn't you?" Mrs. Marsan tried to break the tension.

"The Travelers' Aid found this one for me. I was staying there."

"Come from far?"

"A little town in Illinois."

"Folks there?"

"Only a married sister."

"She must have hated to see you leave."

Jean looked up.

"I don't know."

"Didn't she say?"

"I left a note. I thought it was better than saying good-by."

"Well," Mrs. Marsan considered, "it might have been easier but I don't know if it was better."

"Her husband came home. And I couldn't stand it. I just couldn't stand it!"

Mrs. Marsan sighed. "I guess that was only human—at your age. How old are you?"

"Twenty-two."

"So you've come to New York to start over again. I certainly admire your courage."

"It's not courage," Jean said quickly. "It's cowardice. I know that."

She's honest . . . and smart. . . .

"I couldn't bear it," Jean hurried on. "Everything hurt—people and things and everything. I just wanted to be alone."

"Listen, honey. There's enough loneliness in this world without you manufacturing more. If you wanted to shut yourself up you should have gone to a convent, not come to New York."

Jean stared at her.

"You can't go sneaking through life the way you sneaked into this building. It's not always dark. The world's not that accommodating."

"I don't want anybody's questions," Jean said miserably. "I don't want anybody's sympathy."

"The rate you're going, you'll come in for a lot more questions than you reckon on. And as for sympathy, don't worry about being smothered in it. People have enough troubles of their own without nursing yours."

Nobody had spoken to her like this before. Jean listened, trembling and flushed with a vague stirring of indignation.

"And I don't think you deserve too much sympathy," Mrs. Marsan went on. "If you ask me, I think you're putting on a real selfish act that if you were younger you ought to be spanked for. Loosen up and look around. That's the only way to lick what's licking you. You can't do it by making a big company out of Me Myself and hogging the market in touchy feelings."

That's some speech, Lily. If you had to do it all over again, I bet you couldn't. But this girl needs medicine. It's nasty but it's necessary.

"If you ask *me*—"

"I wasn't asking you," Jean said coldly, her eyes alive, her nostrils dilating.

That's good. *Fight!*

"Well, I don't mind telling you the same as if you had. You ought to get out and get a job and make yourself meet people. Get out and study life. It's a bigger subject than your own insides. And while we're on the subject of your insides, you ought to see a doctor. It's not natural for a young girl like you to be skinny as a snapbean and the same color. You ought to get more food and some comfort. And laugh. And fall in love again. If you *have* to act crazy, do it in a way that'll give somebody else some fun besides yourself."

Jean bit her lips to keep them still. A hot strangeness stung the rims of her eyes.

And now for the final slap in the face that will wake her up and bring her out of it. Steady, Lily. You've gone this far. You might as well finish it.

"Anyway, your husband was brave. He wasn't afraid to fight. He didn't run away from people and things, even if they were krauts and bullets. He must think you're a pretty poor soldier."

The blow told. Jean jumped up and fled into the living room. She threw herself on the sofa and began to cry uncontrollably. She felt as if the tears came from her toes, a flood sweeping away the hard mass in her chest. It felt good to cry. A physical relief that was almost sensual caught her in a wave and carried her away and out of herself.

"You have a good session now, honey," Mrs. Marsan said. "Get it out of your system. And then when you're feeling better we'll have a nice lunch and talk about what you're going to do."

She returned to the kitchen and began emptying the bags.

Maybe if she mixed the spinach up with enough meat Lady would eat it. The dewy green leaves melted into a blur before her. She reached in her bosom for her handkerchief. It was many a year since she had thought of Louis. She wondered if the first man a woman loves ever really dies.

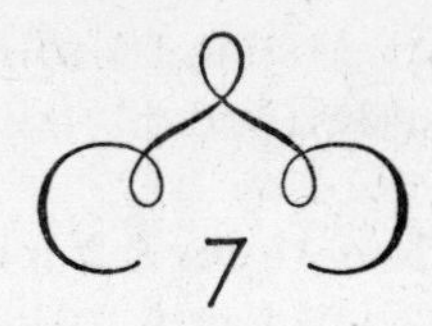

A WHOLE week passed before Mrs. Marsan found time to paste anything in her scrapbook. She was in the habit of clipping bits out of the newspaper, particularly the Daily Watchword. These she glued in a patchwork pattern on the pages of a looseleaf binder embellished with gilt scrolls, a twenty-five-cent bargain from Woolworth's.

The inspiration Mrs. Marsan drew from the Daily Watchword was equaled only by her faith in the Daily Horoscope. Eagerly she read the quotation this morning, and thoroughly she agreed. *The sound of a kiss is not so loud as that of cannon, but its echo lasts a great deal longer.*—OLIVER WENDELL HOLMES. Her scissors performed a neat operation on the column and the excerpt was pasted prominently at the top of a new page. She read again the General Tendencies part of the horoscope: "Excellent today for most purposes, unless you get up too late in the morning, for the finest forces seem to dawn early just now. Try this date for romance." Mrs. Marsan wondered if having gotten up at eight o'clock was too late, the forecast being unspecific on this point. If anything was not excellent today, it was, of course, because she had not gotten up soon enough.

The planetary aspects had worked out in a truly marvelous way during the last few days. The sun entering Scorpio the final week in October had precipitated a time of misunderstandings and mistakes; but as soon as this initial phase was over, everything straightened out smooth as silk. Mr. Ingalls was the only one who had fared badly and that only in a financial way; he probably thought the outcome worth the cost.

Mr. Cernak was finally out of jail, having finally talked himself into it. Added to the charges already against him was another for contempt of court. He had dared to call the police "henchmen of American politics," and to lecture the judge on Mammon and human machines. He then refused to pay the fine and when Mr. Ingalls paid it for him he said it was another example of swindling and serfdom.

Mr. Ingalls would not accept Mr. Cernak's reimbursement. He claimed, as in court, that he was responsible for the whole business from the beginning. He paid Duffy's fine, and doubled the five that had inspired the job. All this including the ten dollars' damages entered by Sig must have put Mr. Ingalls back a whole month's salary.

It had, however, put him considerably forward in Miss Larsch's esteem, or at least brought him within the circle of her gratitude. It was Mrs. Marsan herself who made sure that Adrian learned all the details. It was rarely that anyone could catch Adrian, who was always in a rush, and Mrs. Marsan thought she had better squeeze the sponge of the present opportunity dry by bringing up Mr. Ingalls' accurate acquaintance with Browning. "He says it's not *the* prostrate ghost. It's *each* prostrate ghost." On her next trip to the store Mrs. Marsan found out that Adrian had allowed Mr. Ingalls to give her *Philip II*. That was two and a half to three dollars more.

Though he seemed happier than ever before, Mrs. Marsan felt sorry for Mr. Ingalls. She particularly regretted that, far from her original hopes for him, he was not only without a bedfellow but now without a bed. A young bachelor like that sleeping on a cheap canvas folding-cot, alone, was to her mind a two-edged deprivation. It was all the more ironic that she who in imagination had provided him with a sweetheart was the very one who had despoiled him even of his sheets. "Jean is sleeping in Mr. Ingalls' bed after all," she had said to Mr. Cernak. There was a kind of poetic justice about it.

Mr. Ingalls had responded more handsomely than any to Mr. Cernak's call to share the wealth. He needed a new studio couch anyway, he said, the leg of this one being loose; and he might have meant it if he had not had to share his wealth also with the police department. Joey and Edna had more dishes than they needed. Coral Sands contributed a rug and a clock. Jessamine produced pots and pans she never used. Adrian Larsch gave three pictures—copies of Manet, Renoir and Degas. Mrs. Marsan remembered she had a breakfast table and two chairs stored away in Doc Kincaid's cellar; Doc sandpapered, scrubbed and varnished them—with materials Mrs. Marsan furnished, for Doc was already stretching his capacity for sharing when he threw in his time. Elvira sent up a rubber plant and a mirror. The Brinkmanns had a floor lamp; all it needed was a shade. Vivien Villars gave clothes, including a furred coat. They were beautiful things, good materials, cut to perfection, and they fitted Jean as if they had always been hers. "I've grown out of them," Vivien said wearily. The tar-paper packages came down from the closet shelves. Vivien said she was glad to get rid of them.

Somewhere the Daily Watchword quoted a Chinese proverb which Mrs. Marsan had adopted. *Never take off your shoes till you come to the river.* It had proved its wisdom once again. Any excess worry about having destroyed Miss Larsch's note when Sig put out another wreck would have been wasted; for Sig, called upon to share, had surrendered the chair. He could have done better; yet Mrs. Marsan found more cause to rejoice than to criticize. It was a piece of luck not only for her, but for Mr. Ingalls and Mr. Kennedy, who was saved from being pestered with further complaints. Jean drew the least advantage from the transfer because she would have to buy a cretonne cover.

Even Hannah profited, for if she had been sitting in the chair nursing Maxie instead of leaning against the mailbox doing it when that trained nurse came up to drop in a letter, she never would have known about the asafetida. Licorice, quinine, garlic, even pepper she had tried, but Maxie had a precocious appreciation of flavors. Since the asafetida he cringed if Hannah so much as made a motion to unbutton her blouse.

Mrs. Marsan pasted in the last Watchword and was preparing to put the papers on the pile for the junkman when an advertisement jumped up and struck her in the eye. "Get your Christmas selling job at Macy's. Apply at the Red Door." It was like an answer to a letter. She could almost see "Dear Jean" written at the head of it. Her scissors snipped it out greedily.

It was wonderful, the way things worked out if you let them. She had cut out so many Watchwords that she could make them up herself. "You can't work *everything* out alone," she said. "If you didn't leave some things for God to do, He'd be out of a job."

Before closing the scrapbook she looked at the horoscope again. ". . . for romance." It might be a good day to see Doc Kincaid about Lady and Lord Dundee.

2

Doc was in the cellar sweeping. The odd pieces of rubbish he saved were piled in a corner as if he intended to put a match to them at last and the place looked as bare as an empty box.

"The goals go up there and there," Doc said, swinging his broom back and front. "Lucky there're no windows else I wouldn't have it."

"I thought he was only going to have ping-pong, tenpins and quoits." The dust got in her nose and Mrs. Marsan sneezed. "Didn't know he figured on basket ball."

"He's figuring on a punching bag and wrestling, too. I'm sorry I ever agreed to it."

Doc's mouth sagged and his mustache drooped mournfully. He was a lean man with graying reddish hair and eyes that looked sharp even though they had the watery softness of oysters.

"They can't make any more noise down in the cellar than they make out on the sidewalk," Mrs. Marsan consoled him.

She knew Doc Kincaid would never have agreed to Mr. Cernak's Place-to-Play Movement from the beginning if it had not been for the feud with Sig. Since the first day of the drugstore there had been a competitive undercurrent between Doc and Sig for the ice-cream, soda and candy trade. If Doc had the boys in his basement it was unlikely that they would spend their nickels for chocolate and cones anywhere but upstairs. And playing would make them thirsty. The fountain could stand more popularity than it was presently enjoying.

While a shrewd business sense stimulated Doc, Mr. Cernak's motive was a matter of pride and policy combined. Since Mr. Ingalls staunchly refused to be repaid, Mr. Cernak decided that the penalty money should go to some constructive purpose; he felt it ignoble either to keep it or use it for his own convenience. He did not hesitate in face of the fact that he, an assistant bookkeeper, could scarcely afford to throw money away; neither could Mr. Ingalls. Mr. Cernak had a strong interest in boys, particularly the teen-age type that roamed the streets. They would be the men who would eventually effect the Utopia of a united brotherhood and an equalized economy. They must, Mr. Cernak felt, be fitted for tomorrow's fight. He thought wistfully of an arena a hundred times larger than Doc Kincaid's cellar, of hockey, skating and football; but he was glad he had been able to make Doc see, through the cash register, that the cellar should be conceded without a demand for rent.

"I hear somebody in the drugstore. I'd better go up."

Doc laid his broom in a corner and followed Mrs. Marsan and Lady up the few steps to the sidewalk. Mrs. Marsan remembered her mission. She made it plain and brief to Doc as they went in.

"That terrier's a pedigreed dog. Usually I get ten dollars but I'll make it five for you," Doc bargained. "And first choice of the pups. That's the rule."

Vivien Villars was in the drugstore.

"Five and first choice if there *are* pups," Mrs. Marsan haggled. "Nothing if nothing."

"That's not the rule," Doc insisted. "You ask any kennel—"

"I wouldn't send Lady to any kennel."

"She's pretty old." Doc Kincaid considered Lady. "She's likely to miss out on the litter anyway and I lose the pup."

"Because she's likely to miss out is just why you shouldn't charge five dollars."

"I've got to realize *something* on my investment." Doc was indignant. "Seems to me I've been seeing that dog around here a pretty long time. How old is she anyway?"

"Seven," Mrs. Marsan admitted.

"That's five more than my terrier."

"Oh, all right then." Mrs. Marsan shrugged her billowy shoulders. "Five and first choice."

"These May and December deals hardly ever turn out

right," Doc grumbled. "She's too old for him. But anyway—"

"I'll let you know if and when," Mrs. Marsan concluded.

Vivien was leaning against the counter, still and stone gray.

Doc's manner indicated that Vivien bought expensive drugs in continuous quantities. He forced himself to be friendly and polite, and put on a smile a couple of sizes too large.

"Sorry to keep you waiting. Wonderful weather, don't you think? How's Mr. Villars?"

A wan light came to Vivien's face.

"Burt is fine," she said fondly.

"Something I can do for you?" The smile stretched.

She had a prescription which she wanted filled at once. She wanted to know how long it would take.

Mrs. Marsan noticed that her hair needed doing. It was frowsed out as if she had had a sleepless night and the false part showed pepper-and-salt at the roots. She was putting on weight, too. There was a doughy bulge around the ungirdled waist.

"About half an hour, twenty minutes," Doc said.

"Send it up, will you?"

"If I can find somebody to send." Doc was not noted for his quickness to oblige, no matter how good the customer was.

"I'll bring it," Mrs. Marsan offered. "I'll be up in about half an hour."

Vivien looked grateful.

"I'll leave the door open. Just walk right in. I'm going back to bed."

She was sick again. She was certainly staying home a lot lately.

Mrs. Marsan had a two-dollar bet to place at Sig's, now that Donegan was out of sight. She hoped Sig would have some good tips. Perhaps the "excellent" in today's horoscope included luck with horses. By the time she came back the prescription would be ready.

3

A painful tightening in the chest reminded Mrs. Marsan to stop midway up the stairs and catch her breath. Leaning against the rail she read the directions on the bottle: One three times a day for five days eight days before. She read the label again, puffing harder with the effort of figuring it out. At length she gave it up, annoyed at her failure. Directions like that were enough to make a sick person worse.

Vivien heard her weighted step in the hall and called "Come in!" from the bedroom.

"Five dollars for a bit of a bottle like this," Mrs. Marsan said. "Drugstores are a stick-up."

Vivien raised herself on an elbow, reached for the chain and jerked the bedlamp to life. The soft glow fanned out over twin satin pillows.

"It's not really expensive. Considering what it does." She uncapped it and drew out the rope of cotton.

"There's more wadding in it than pills," Mrs. Marsan observed.

Her eyes wandered about the room. At the moment she was more interested in what Pearl described as symptoms than in any symptoms Vivien might describe. A deep-rose carpet lay thick on the floor. The lamp on the bedside table wore a lighter rose shade; even the ceiling fixture was in a subduing silk bonnet. It must be pretty in here at night, Mrs. Marsan thought, with the rose glow doubled in the mirrors —pretty and romantic as a rose itself. And if, as Pearl claimed, satin was a symptom, then this was a very bad case; for the bed was a sea of it. Mrs. Marsan had never seen such a spread; its shirred flounces fell over the side to the floor, and it lay in thick creamy clouds where Vivien had thrown it back toward the foot. The foot—Pearl was right. There was no foot. Only something long and low and tufted, like a bench, stood against the bed at its open end.

"I've got to take one of these right away." Vivien fell back on the pillow. "Good God, my head! . . ." She closed her eyes, reaching up blindly to put out the bedlamp.

"Wait a minute. I'll get you some water."

A pyramid of dishes was piled up in the kitchen sink. Yesterday was Wednesday and Pearl must have straightened up, but not a glass had been washed since then. This morning's breakfast spoke from the topmost plate: a curl of ham rind and the waxy yellow traces of fried eggs. Mrs. Marsan put the plate down for Lady, who had followed her in. She looked for the second breakfast plate with possible scraps but there was only the one.

"You must have found things pretty much upset," Vivien said when she returned with the water.

"I didn't notice anything," Mrs. Marsan lied gracefully.

Vivien shook out one of the pellets which were like little brown beans. After taking it she reached in the drawer of the night table and pulled out a small calendar in a leather cover with a tiny pencil attached and put a circle around the date.

"Before I forget." She hid the calendar way back in the drawer and pushed it closed. "If I lose count and take these pills for more than five days a month," she said with an effort at gaiety, "I'm likely to start bleating like a sheep."

"You don't say!" Mrs. Marsan's surprise shoved her to the point. "What're they for?"

Vivien hesitated. Then, because she was sick and lonely and afraid, she felt suddenly glad to talk to a woman who was older—ever so much older, she amended, with a throb of triumph.

"It's hormatone," Vivien said. "I looked it up in a medical dictionary in the doctor's waiting room the other day. It comes from a Greek word, *hormon,* something that excites or puts in motion."

Mrs. Marsan looked at the bottle on the night table with heightened interest.

"What has it got to do with a sheep?"

"It's extracted from sheep."

"Doing you any good?"

"I don't know. Sometimes I think it is, and sometimes I don't. These sick headaches almost kill me."

"Maybe if you could sleep," Mrs. Marsan suggested.

"That's just it. I can't sleep. Night or day, I'm as jumpy as a cricket. I hear the least little noise, and it bothers me. And lying awake I have the sensation of things creeping on my skin. Sometimes I think I'm going insane."

"I went through all that," Mrs. Marsan comforted. "It'll wear off."

Vivien's face on the big pillow looked little and shrunken, her eyes weirdly large.

"The doctor doesn't think it's that," she said hollowly. "He said all I need is toning up."

"Maybe he thinks it will worry you. Maybe he thinks you won't be glad. I've heard some women aren't."

"It's my thyroid!" Vivien clenched her hands and almost screamed it. "I know it is! I've told him so a dozen times! That's why I feel so sluggish and numb and depressed. That's why I'm gaining—no matter how little or how carefully I eat!"

"I used to get dizzy and see spots," Mrs. Marsan recalled. "And such a logginess—my head felt like a barrel of cement. Sometimes I'd be burning up in the face and a little while afterwards I'd be icy cold in sweat."

Vivien stared at her, dully fascinated. For some odd reason

her eyes fixed on the lobe of Mrs. Marsan's ear. It was large and fat and flabby, hanging like an old breast. Automatically Vivien's hand went up to her own ear. She fancied the lobe was less firm and elastic than it used to be. A frantic need to be rid of Mrs. Marsan blinded her.

"Well, thank you for all your trouble. Just close the door as you go out, will you?"

"I can't leave you with those dishes to do," Mrs. Marsan objected. "I'll do them before I go."

Vivien had carefully forgotten about the dishes. Now a smoke of nausea choked her when she thought of the greasy plates and the stale smell of coffee grounds. No matter how she felt she had always managed to get Burt his meals, and to keep things clean and comfortable for him to come home to. She would get those dishes washed even if it killed her.

"No, thank you just the same. I'll feel better in a few hours."

Mrs. Marsan was already on her way to the kitchen. "Don't be foolish. They won't take a minute."

Vivien could never lie down for long. That was part of it. Even the clink and clack of the dishes jarred her. Impatiently she got out of bed and went to her vanity.

She sat down and searched herself in the wing of the mirror, anxiously fingering her earlobe. It's silly, she kept thinking—one of those buzzing fears about growing old that were beginning to plague her like flies. She reached for her rouge pad and passed it over the pale tip of her ear; then she brought one of her diamond studs out of her jewel box and screwed it tentatively into place. There, she smiled; sparkling dew on a rose petal. That was Burt's remark a long time ago, when she wore them for the first time and said, "Look what I've bought to make me prettier for you." It was worth every dollar of the price, the way Burt had loved her in them. "You look like a duchess, Viv. I'm so proud of you—"

Maybe she would wear them tonight. She had to be brilliant and beautiful again for Burt's birthday. She had to feel his old pride pricking her pleasantly in the back as she followed the waiter to a ringside table. They would have champagne with their dinner and they would be gay and Burt's hand would be hot and hard over hers as they danced. Everything would be the way it was in the beginning. . . .

The room blacked out before her. She groped to the bed and fell across it, lying quite still, blaming her eyes. She ought to investigate the new contact lenses she saw advertised. "Be glamorous with invisible glasses. . . ."

Mrs. Marsan appeared as a cloud, saying: "Well, I'm through. I swept and tidied up a bit."

Vivien thanked her. "It's Burt's birthday today. We're going out to dinner, but he hates an upset kitchen all the same."

"You ought to see Mr. Ingalls' kitchen," Mrs. Marsan said. "I went in to warm over some coffee I'd brought him once and it was so snowed under I couldn't find the stove."

"Would you like to see what I got for Burt?" Vivien pointed to the blot which was the vanity. "Look in the top right-hand drawer."

"In this blue velvet box?" Mrs. Marsan was eager. She opened it before waiting for an answer. "My, that's beautiful! A wrist watch like that must have cost more than two hundred dollars!"

She waited for Vivien to state the price, to a penny. But Vivien merely smiled.

"Burt is worth the world," she said.

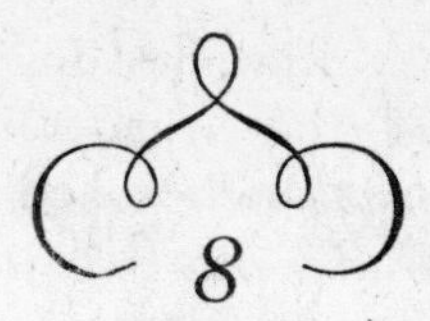

8

MRS. MARSAN had a dress of her own to add to the collection the Reverend Frankel brought Joey to repair. Buttons and darning were required before some of the worn clothing given by the church ladies could be sent to Europe. Mrs. Marsan had persuaded Jean Landry to lend a hand.

"He say they so hard up they mightn't even have needle and thread." Pearl held a brush and a dustpan containing a white powder and several rigid roaches. "But he say so much you got to believe only half. When a man talk and talk like that he just *can't* be telling the truth *all* the time."

"What's that?" Mrs. Marsan asked, looking at the dustpan.

"Borax," Pearl croaked. She managed a pantomime which, interpreted, meant "Miss Edna's putting down borax and sugar again and there're some dead ones. Don't tell Miss Joey."

By the front window, Joey was looking out on the naked November afternoon through Mr. Cernak's opera glasses. The sky threatened rain or snow. Joey wheeled around when she heard voices.

"Jean's come to help," Mrs. Marsan said. "And I brought the book to read. And some of my own coffee, with chicory in it. And my own dripper. So we can have a cup of the real by and by."

"It's a shame to make you sew on your first visit." Joey was so excited about Jean she trembled.

"I don't mind," Jean said tonelessly.

"Don't you love dogs?" Lady had put her paws on Joey's knees, and Joey leaned over and stroked her with both hands.

Jean did not answer.

"You keep her out of the kitchen, Pearl." Mrs. Marsan gave Pearl a meaning look. "Not everything agrees with her delicate stomach."

"Did she—?" Joey's eyes questioned Mrs. Marsan.

"I saw Doc Kincaid. Lady's engaged."

"You better not tell Miss Edna you figuring on getting a puppy in this here apartment," Pearl advised.

Joey clenched her hands in Lady's kinks.

"Once it's here, she'll *have* to let me keep it!"

"Miss Edna your sister," Pearl sniffed, screwing her face up to one side, "but I know her better than you." She left the room to get the minister's bundle.

"I brought a donation." Mrs. Marsan held up her black crêpe. It was the one in the lap of which Lady had left the gleam that was not gold. "It's got a mark on it, but otherwise it's almost brand-new. From all I hear about how much they get to eat, they can take out the whole front and still have a dress."

"That's a nice one," Joey said. "I like that breast pocket with the zipper. And there are some stout people over there yet. Not all of them are thin in the papers."

"Maybe you're right. I always say, it's not what you eat. It's who you are. If God says He wants you to be big don't talk back at Him with all this dieting and massage and monkey business."

"Lots of ladies over at that church not talking back." Pearl deposited the opened bundle on the table. "Those poor Misplaced Persons certainly going to be misplaced in some of *these* outsizes."

She brought the sewing basket and pushed the bundle aside to make room for it.

"What would you rather do, Jean—mend or sew buttons?" Joey was thinking, she's just three years older than I and a woman of the world already. She sighed.

"It doesn't matter," Jean said.

"Well," Mrs. Marsan put a piece off the table in Jean's lap, "you can do some of both. Help yourself to what you need out of the basket."

Mrs. Marsan regretted that Jean had showed no enthusiasm about applying at Macy's Red Door to get her selling job. She was disappointed, but not discouraged. At least she had succeeded in dragging Jean with her to Dr. Crowell. She must remember to make her keep the next appointment, and to investigate whether or not she was taking the vitamins. As for Jean's getting out and mingling with people, she would see to that. Today was only the beginning.

"I'll sew the buttons," Pearl said. "Me, I'd rather die than darn. My sister Edie—can *she* darn! But not my sister Bella. She can't even stitch a button in the right place. And Madam sews buttons and darns too!" She looked at Jean, her china-ball eyes big and unbelieving.

Jean did not recognize herself as Madam. Quietly, she was threading a needle.

"Pearl, don't go looking for symptoms," Mrs. Marsan said. "What I told you that time is all a mistake. Mr. Ingalls is in love with Miss Larsch."

"Good Lord, is he?" Pearl seemed to pale.

"Miss Larsch is all right. She gave Pearl an opera program for me the other day. But she's not as nice as—" Joey stopped in mid-air. "What I mean is—she'd never have time to sew a button for anybody but herself." She studied Jean with new eyes. Jean wasn't a woman of the world after all. It was too bad, and yet it was better.

"So he in love with Miss Larsch. . . . Whew!" Pearl whistled under her breath. "Downright bad I don't know that earlier— He sure got a mess on his hand now." She shook her head and shuddered.

"Let's hope it'll soon be on his knee.—Well, do you want to hear more of the story?"

Mrs. Marsan had finished reading them *Sappho* and a few weeks before started on *Tess of the D'Urbervilles.* It was her own book and they could linger over it as long as they liked. Since the evening Edna came and forbade Mrs. Marsan to lend Joey what she called "that kind of book" because it gave Joey what Edna termed "impossible ideas" and Mrs. Marsan had promised faithfully never to do it again, the afternoon literary sessions had been inaugurated. Mrs. Marsan did not promise Edna she would never read the books to Joey aloud.

"Where were we?" She wet her thumb and spanked through the pages. "I got a pencil put here but I don't believe it's the right place."

"We were where Tess going to that place out in the country somewheres to mind the old lady's chickens."

"I thought we passed 'Phase the First, The Maiden.' Didn't we start 'Phase the Second, Maiden No More'?"

"No, we didn't go that far," Joey said. "I would have remembered."

"Here we are! I remember now. The bell rang and we thought it was Edna and I just had time to mark a scratch. Alec picked Tess up in his buggy and they were riding along a deserted road, page sixty-five."

"I remember now, too! He wanted her to kiss him!" Joey stuck her finger.

"Lessee did she," Pearl said.

"Well, here goes. 'He was inexorable, and she sat still, and D'Urberville'—that's Alec—'gave her the kiss of mastery. No sooner had he done so than she flushed with shame, took out her handkerchief, and wiped the spot on her cheek—' "

"Her *cheek!*" screamed Pearl.

"That's what it says." Mrs. Marsan looked again. "Her cheek."

"Good Lord, what wrong with her mouth?" Pearl fussed. "Any man kiss me on *my* cheek, I slap his face."

"Hush up, Pearl," Joey said.

" '—wiped the spot on her cheek that had been touched by his lips. His ardor was nettled at the sight . . .' "

She read on while the others sewed. It was dark already at four o'clock and they had to light the lamp. There were only a couple of pages more before the end of "Phase the First" and Joey had to know what happened to Tess when Alec caught her alone late at night in the forest.

"He knelt and bent lower, till her breath warmed his face, and in a moment his cheek was in contact with hers. . . . Darkness and silence ruled everywhere around. Above them rose the primeval yews and oaks of The Chase. . . . Where was Tess's guardian angel? Where was the providence of her simple faith? . . . Why it was that upon this beautiful feminine tissue, sensitive as gossamer, and practically blank as snow as yet, there should have been traced such a coarse pattern as it was doomed to receive; why so often the coarse appropriates the finer thus, the wrong man the woman, the wrong woman the man, many thousand years of analytical philosophy have failed to explain to our sense of order. . . . As Tess's own people down in those retreats are never tired of saying among each other in their fatalistic way: 'It was to be.' There lay the pity of it. An immeasurable social chasm was to divide our heroine's personality thereafter from that previous self of hers who stepped from her mother's door to try her fortune at Trantridge poultry-farm."

Mrs. Marsan drew a long breath and closed the book.

"That's the end of the first part," she said. "And the next is 'Phase the Second, Maiden No More.' "

"There's too much words to that," Pearl complained. "I wish instead of so much words they'd told exactly what *happened*."

"But Pearl, you *know* what happened," Joey said.

"I know I know. But I rather be told."

Jean had hardly spoken since she came. Mrs. Marsan wondered if she had heard a shred of the story. She continued stitching away diligently even after the book was closed. Indeed, she had done most of the work, for Pearl and Joey frequently stopped to enjoy their excitement.

Pearl went to put the water on for the coffee. Joey was folding finished pieces. The pencil rolled out of the book into Mrs. Marsan's lap. It was the finger of Fate, she thought, pointing to an idea. She tore out the flyleaf and carefully printed "Write Jean Landry," including the address. This she stealthily put in the pocket of the donated black crêpe and zipped the pocket closed.

2

Coral Sands needed fifty dollars.

"I've got a hundred, but the course I want is a hundred and a half."

"If Miami Moon had come in today I could have let you have it," Mrs. Marsan said ruefully. "Sig's been handing me a straight line of stinkers lately. I ought to quit."

"Oh, I guess I could get it." Coral lounged back in a corner of the sofa and pensively pulled on a strand of her bright hair. "Only I wanted it right away. I wanted to start tomorrow."

"Where did you get the hundred?"

"Sold my leopard skin coat."

"Again?"

"I'm sick of it anyway. It was getting to look like a lemon with the leprosy."

"I thought you traded that coat in on the new one." Mrs. Marsan looked at the Persian lamb lying lushly over the back of Mr. Cernak's chair.

"Marsie, you old liar. You know damn well you didn't think that." Coral reproached her through long sweeping lashes.

"Well," Mrs. Marsan shrugged, "you've got only one life to live and there's only one person can live it for you."

"You spilled a bucketful!" Coral agreed. "Not everybody sees it that way."

"Couldn't you get the fifty where you got the fur coat?—Not that I'm advising you to!" she tacked on.

"No. I don't know what's the matter with me, but my interest don't hold up as well as it used to." Her eyes grew dreamy. "It's funny. . . ."

"I guess you're getting old," Mrs. Marsan said with a smear of good-natured sarcasm.

"You said it. Next time I better shake down a set of false teeth.—No, all cracks aside, Marsie, I've got to take this course. It's a matter of life and death. I study and survive or answer ads and starve. This modeling course will put me on the right track."

"Where did you get all this stuff."

Mrs. Marsan was leafing through the literature on her lap. *Exciting Courses in the Mastery of the Mannequin Art . . . Showroom Psychology and Technique . . . Romance of the*

Retail Salon . . . Glorious Road to Glamour . . . The girl on the magazine cover may be you. . . .

"Burt Villars got Vivien to get it for me. She had a friend who took the course and made good."

"Well, I guess it couldn't hurt you."

"Two hundred a week couldn't either. Do you realize models earn that much? It might even mean Hollywood. *Anything* is possible."

As a model you move in a magic circle where charm and chic reign supreme, where hushed voices, bright lights and lovely music pay thrilling homage to your breath-taking beauty. . . . Mrs. Marsan turned the page. *To model is to create for yourself a career in a world of constant wonder, to cast off the burden of boredom for a life in which every hour is packed with opportunity and endless adventure. . . .*

"Burt got me an appointment for an interview and I went and they looked me over and said I had everything."

"Everything but the price."

"They said they could probably get me some modeling to do even while I was studying. I could make up the fifty in a couple of hours."

And when with the perfect poise to be acquired through this course you stand in the spotlight with cameras and admiration trained on your elegance, you will be conscious of an allure and polished gentility that is forever yours. . . . Mrs. Marsan sighed. "It sounds nice," she said.

There was a long silence.

"I could even earn enough to improve my voice and dancing. I know now. I'm too green for that game yet. And I'm fed up with these champagne chances. You think you're landing a job and all you've landed is some jerk who's not even connected with the show business. I'm so tired of these plugged dimes I could howl. Maybe it's true. I'm aging."

"I was thinking," Mrs. Marsan said abstractedly. "You know those opera glasses of Mr. Cernak's?"

"What about them?" Coral frowned, trying to fix the connection.

"They're something special. They have gold in them. And Mr. Cernak believes in sharing private property, so he wouldn't mind."

Coral sat up, interested.

"I bet you could get fifty dollars on them easy. From Sobel. You know Sobel?"

"That louse." Coral's mouth twisted bitterly. "He got my bracelet."

"Of course you'd have to redeem them before the time was up."

"I could wring a roll out of that coat," Coral looked at the Persian lamb, "if it was summertime."

"Well, Joey Brent would miss the glasses, too, but I guess we can manage."

Coral smiled happily.

"You're sure Mr. Cernak wouldn't mind?"

Mrs. Marsan went and got the opera glasses.

3

It was nearly eleven when Coral left. "I've got to get over to Brinkmann's for a few things before he closes up," she said.

Mrs. Marsan harnessed Lady for her last airing of the day and the three of them met again on the stairs. Coral had an empty milk bottle in her hand.

A wind like a cat-o'-nine-tails whipped the street and Mrs. Marsan tied her fascinator more snugly around her head and decided she would not take Lady far. She allowed her to sniff around Sig's paper stand, popular with the neighborhood pets, and to pause for a moment under the mailbox. She did the tour of the block from the corner. In the beauty salon a cold blue neon light showed that the clock was about ten minutes slow and the New Magicurl Exclusive at Elvira's was the Most Flattering to the Full Face. Doc's scientific display always depressed her; the snakes of spirochetes and the screws and sticks and balls of bacteria and viruses made repulsive pictures, and tall jars of senna pods and nux vomica did nothing for the appetite. Sig's school tablets and boxes of crayons and toys needed dusting, and one airplane had a weak wing.

Mr. Brinkmann's window was the best on the block. The corners were brightened by placards showing pretty girls, hypocritically slim, drinking beer before beautiful platters of rich sandwiches. The center was graced by a fat plaster pig, with a string of pork sausages slung around his neck. On each side packages of crackers and cookies that lured with cellophane faces were piled in neat pyramids. Mrs. Marsan wondered suddenly if Mr. Brinkmann had gotten in the fresh *schwarzbrot* and went inside.

It was cozy and warm in Mr. Brinkmann's and the smells were something to make a stone drip water. Mrs. Marsan studied the artistry of the potato-salad-mayonnaise with the eye of a connoisseur. Long slices of fat bacon rippled over the baked beans. The pickled herring, spiced and silvery, gleamed with transparent moons of thin onion. Even Lady loved to come in here, for Mr. Brinkmann was fond of dogs and always threw her a taste of whatever he was slicing.

Mr. Brinkmann was a robust man with a yellow mustache and yellow hair that was getting white over the ears. He always seemed gay, whether he was or not, and he sang a great deal. People imposed on him for favors, such as sending over their orders and remembering to save their milk and minding their babies while they ran down the street to the A&P to get for a penny cheaper something he had on his shelves; but Mr. Brinkmann, if it ever occurred to him to be resentful, forgave them all.

Tonight there were several other late customers besides Coral and it was some time before Mr. Brinkmann got to her and Mrs. Marsan. Then nobody else came and they were alone.

"Have you heard how Mrs. Willars is?" He had trouble pronouncing *v* and always said *s* with a short hiss.

Coral's expression alerted.

"Is something the matter?" Mrs. Marsan asked quickly. *Come to think of it I don't remember them coming home this evening.*

"You know the nurse that lives in the neighborhood? The one that told Hannah about what to make Maxie disgusted?" Mr. Brinkmann threw a disc of bologna over the counter to Lady. "She was in here a while ago and she said just before she got off duty a lady got brought to the hospital called Willars and it must be around here because she heard the address. So I said, *Donner!* that's right upstairs nearly on top of my head."

"What happened?" Mrs. Marsan's heart pounded. She sat down on some cartons of canned goods.

"She fainted or some kind of spell at her work."

"Well, I'm not surprised." Mrs. Marsan wagged her head. "She's been sick straight along."

"I thought she was looking bad a long time. Just the other day I said to my wife, Emma, I said, Mrs. Willars is not looking good."

Mr. Brinkmann could offer nothing beyond that.

Mrs. Marsan forgot entirely what she came in for and excused herself for charging a pound of potato salad with the thought that she could not go out without buying something. She meant to sit up and wait for Burt to come home so she could ask him what happened and how Vivien was, and since it was a long time since she had supper the potato salad would make a nice snack.

Coral paid and picked up her bag. She was strangely solemn.

Mrs. Marsan did not have to wait for Burt because Burt himself was waiting on the sidewalk. He threw his cigarette away and stood there with his hands deep in his overcoat pockets.

"Is it true Vivien's in the hospital?" Mrs. Marsan asked without preliminaries. "How is she?"

"Oh, she's all right. It's nothing serious." He was looking at Coral, or rather at her coat. His eyes scowled up from her knees to her shoulders and down again.

"What happened?" Mrs. Marsan persisted.

"Nothing happened," Burt said testily. "She just took a fainting spell, that's all. She's been doing too much lately. The doctor says she's got to lie in for a while for a complete rest." He turned to Coral, giving Mrs. Marsan half his back. "Did you get started at the studio?" His voice was sharp.

"Not yet. Maybe tomorrow."

There was a charged silence. Coral twisted the top of her bag and the paper gave off crackling noises like fire. Mrs. Marsan knew she was making a crowd.

"Well, I'll say good night. I'm sorry to hear about Vivien. If there's anything I can do—"

"Thank you," Burt said without looking at her. "Good night."

As she went in she heard him turn on Coral. "If you'd think more of getting your career started and less of a damned fur coat maybe you'd get some place!"

Mrs. Marsan hurried Lady upstairs, not bothering to stop midway to catch her breath, and made for the living room window. She opened it a few inches quietly. She could have spared herself the effort of not making noise for Burt and Coral were too busy and loud to have noticed it.

"You're a fine one to talk. After what you told me yourself about you and Vivien!" Coral was husky with rage.

"That's my business!"

"Well, this is mine!"

"All right. Make a damn fool of yourself! Who in the hell cares!"

"Wouldn't you like to know. . . ." She turned to sugar and vinegar. "Wouldn't you like to know who cared enough to give me this coat that's got you crazy."

"You're sending that bastard thing back where it came from. Do you hear?" He reached a hand out to her shoulder and shook her. "Do you hear?"

She wriggled herself free.

"Like hell I am! Since when do I take orders from you?"

"Since now," he said through his teeth. "Since right now."

Coral threw her head back and laughed. Her laughter was hard and bright. The sarcasm in it bit through to the bone.

Burt's hand flew out and flashed with a stinging sound across her mouth. The laughter stopped abruptly.

For a minute they stared at each other, utterly still.

Then Burt turned on his heel and swung into the building. Mrs. Marsan could hear his steps racing on the stairs. A moment after his door slammed.

Coral looked rather pathetic, standing down there by Sig's newsstand hugging her paper bag.

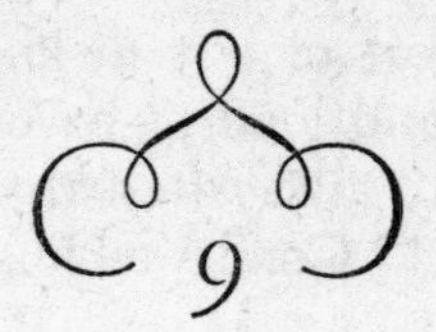

Thanksgiving Day began with wind and rain, but by mid-morning the blustering stopped and the sky cleared to spotless blue. The sun came out shyly, and the air was cold and clean.

Mrs. Marsan rejoiced about the weather. For days she had been having serious talks with herself. You've got to get Jean Landry out of this place on Thanksgiving. You can't let her stick in here thinking about that Thanksgiving in Tampa. . . . It's too bad Miss Larsch won't loosen up a little. She goes lots of places. You'd think she'd get tired of running around alone. . . .

No doubt Mr. Ingalls had hoped to have Thanksgiving dinner with Miss Larsch. He told Mrs. Marsan about it a few mornings before, when she waylaid him on his way to work to hand him a paper bag with two bad eggs. "I'm sorry. We'll replace them," he said. And just then Adrian swept by. The look she gave Mr. Ingalls could not have been occasioned by the pervading odor of the eggs alone; it was that disgusted. Mr. Ingalls flushed. He said she had sent back *Philip II*. "She's heard some ridiculous rumor about—well, about my reputation," he said. "I can't make it out. It came through a person named Pearl."

Mr. Ingalls was so miserable that Mrs. Marsan felt compelled to do something about it. She had not yet decided what. The first thing was to have a talk with Adrian, though catching her was like running after a departed train. In any case, Mrs. Marsan knew it was futile to hope that a hint would land Jean a guarantee against being alone on Thanksgiving Day. Adrian probably had tickets to this or that. She might even give Jean a ticket. She had handed over the pictures pleasantly enough. But to give a minute of her time, or a minute of herself, was beyond the possibilities of Adrian's breathless program.

This morning's paper pointed the way. The horoscope declared the day favorable to entertainment, social affairs and short trips. Almost as if on purpose, the opposite page was a spread advertising a Mammoth, Merry Thanksgiving Parade. Seventeen Floats! Seven Bands! Acrobats, Tumblers, Clowns! Dancers! Animals! Sideshows! And—somewhat prematurely, Santa Claus himself. There was no better means in the world, Mrs. Marsan reflected, to get Jean to mingle with people than a parade on Broadway.

She counted her money and realized ruefully that most of her spare had ridden off on Sig's horses. The only thing fast about Sig's tips was the way the money went. Still she could manage something. It might not be from soup to nuts, but she was sure of from paper napkin to pumpkin pie. The automat was advertising a turkey dinner for seventy-five cents.

First of all she brought Mr. Cernak's opera glasses over to Joey. The way Coral resurrected them on the third day was no less baffling—Mrs. Marsan meant no blasphemy—than the Miracle of the Tomb itself. Coral did not bother to explain beyond "Thanks, Marsie. I'm started on my course and everything's okay."

Edna was home, of course, and Pearl on holiday. You could tell Edna was home from the stamping and swearing in the kitchen. Mrs. Marsan found Joey with a long face despite the presents Edna had lavishly piled up around her. Several roach bodies were laid out on a dustpan bier awaiting mass burial in the garbage can.

The detail of putting down food and water for Lady dispatched, Mrs. Marsan went after Jean. It was dim in the hall, and the front rooms of the back apartments always needed light. The golden bar across Mr. Ingalls' sill, which was getting to be a kind of symbol of him, day and night, lay there in pale concentration. Mrs. Marsan could not help putting her good ear to his door. He was such a quiet man. She heard only a faint friction, as of beans brushing against each other in a bag, and she knew Mr. Ingalls was typing those terrible A&P price lists on the rented noiseless. She shook her head. Maybe Mr. Cernak was right about slaves.

She crossed the hall and knocked on Jean's door.

"I want to go to Times Square and see the parade and I don't dare go up and down all those subway steps by myself," she said. "I was wondering—we could have something to eat somewheres afterwards."

2

They ran into Burt and Coral in the train. Mrs. Marsan pondered in which class of accident to put the fact of these two being together—neatly-thought-out or natural.

Unquestionably not natural was how they sat and the way they talked. Mrs. Marsan thought of the night on the sidewalk and concluded that a slap in the face was sometimes worth two on the back. The good will between Burt and Coral was about all that could be between them, since they were as close as pages in a book though they had vacant space on both sides. They talked in a trance—broken bits of sentences, lazy smiles.

Before the train started Mrs. Marsan had time to ask Burt how Vivien was. He jerked straight, as if astounded that there were other people not only in the world, but actually in the same car.

"She's doing fine, thank you," he said across the aisle.

"When's she coming home?"

"In a few days, I think."

"Well, I know you'll be glad." Mrs. Marsan let her smile spread slowly like molasses. "You must be terribly lonely, to say nothing of the worry."

Casually, Coral moved over an inch. The inch only made it more obvious that there was not a hair's breadth there before.

The doors slid shut and the train started. Jean was not inclined to conversation and Mrs. Marsan succumbed to reading the headlines in the paper to her right. While waiting for the slowpoke to turn the page, she was drawn again to Burt and Coral opposite. There was something provokingly peculiar about both of them; not their attitude after the other night's argument, but something more touchable, more real. Yet she could not put her finger on it.

They had now assumed a cool distance, challenging the public to think they cared a penny whether the one or the other lived or died. Coral was reading the ads from gum to girdles. Burt, his arms crossed, studied the nails of one hand. The difference about Burt was especially annoying, elusive as an eel. Several times Mrs. Marsan thought she had it cornered. It was like having a word on the tip of your tongue. . . .

The newspaper got off, leaving Mrs. Marsan to concentrate entirely on Burt. It was something really remarkable that had happened to him. He looked actually boyish. The brand-new hat, was it? Or the brand-new interest? The hat and the bright eye helped, but there was something besides.

Burt squirmed under the microscope of Mrs. Marsan's scrutiny. Self-consciously he passed his fingers over his upper lip and down over his chin.

Then Mrs. Marsan knew. He had shaved off his mustache. And with it at least ten years.

The difference about Coral lay somehow in a tantalizing

sameness. There was present something as familiar as her face which still had no business being. It tortured Mrs. Marsan for recognition. She itemized Coral, hoping to hit on the answer by a process of elimination. The shiny metallic earrings? No. The orchid? No. Even Coral was not accustomed to wearing orchids and what teased Mrs. Marsan with its strangeness was something Coral was accustomed to do. But if she was accustomed to do it, why should it be strange?

The express rattled out of the tube under the East River, began to eat up stations on the other side. Unless Mrs. Marsan found out soon what was so right about Coral that it made her wrong, they would all be getting off and she would never know.

At the Fifth Avenue stop a woman got on with a Persian lamb just like—

Well, there it was. The answer jumped out at her as if it were alive.

The strangeness was Coral's coat. She was wearing the old leopard again instead of the new lamb.

Promptly Mrs. Marsan started on a piece of mental mosaic. Mr. Cernak's opera glasses redeemed. The leopard skin bought back. The modeling course started. She fitted together the bits and at first it looked as if the missing Persian had paid for everything. Then she added the way Burt and Coral were before the train started, and the nub of the argument the other night. Now the picture showed the lamb sent back instead of sold. And if it was, who or what paid for the other things, including the orchid?

The train stopped and the people herded to the doors. Mrs. Marsan roused Jean.

"This is Times Square. We get out here."

If Burt's salary was sufficient to do so much for Coral, why was it that Vivien always paid bills with her own check? Mrs. Marsan knew because on several occasions she had brought in Vivien's gas and electric with her own and handed Mr. Kennedy the Villars' rent when he came to collect. An idea jabbed at her but it was too late to verify it because Burt was somewhere behind her in the crowd.

She delayed deliberately on the platform and bumped into Burt at the foot of the escalator. Coral had hurried on ahead, protesting "We're not together" more loudly than if she had shouted it.

Mrs. Marsan managed to get between Jean and Burt. She had him now all the way going up. She turned and fixed a friendly face.

"I guess you're going to the hospital."

Burt said "Yes."

"Tell Vivien to hurry up and come home."

"I will, thank you."

"I hope we're not missing that parade." Now for verifying the idea. "Have you got the time?"

Burt looked at his wrist from habit. It was bare. He cleared his throat before answering.

"Sorry. I've forgotten my watch."

Mrs. Marsan knew now who was paying for the orchids and other things. Vivien.

3

The turkey passed, a mastodon bird of painted papier-mâché. The pumpkin was a colossal balloon, leashed on a dozen washlines. Wedged in the mob, Mrs. Marsan admired it all. Even Jean smiled at the dancing clowns, though she took the gay music like medicine.

Mrs. Marsan would have given less attention to the parade if she had known Burt and Coral were only five people to her left.

"Look." Burt, behind Coral, took his hands from her shoulders. "There's the Seeing Eye again."

Coral looked and laughed. "We're haunted."

"I have a notion that when we go to dinner she's going to turn up in our soup."

Coral was stuck against him like a postage stamp on a letter. The mounted police shooed the crowd back from the curb and in the surge he put his arm around her waist to keep her steady.

"Don't let her see us." Coral made herself little.

"What do you say we get out of this?"

"I've had enough," Coral agreed. "Let's go."

They worked to a clear spot around the corner. Through the glass windows they saw people drinking coffee and eating doughnuts. They went in and took a back table and ordered coffee.

"Where will it be for dinner?" Burt lit her cigarette and his. Her lips were soft and smooth. He ached at the sparkle of her youth. It aroused in him an uneasy hunger, caused the pounding of a tiny hammer at his temple.

"Some place that won't be so packed you're likely to chew on your neighbor's arm for a drumstick."

"Coney Island?" Burt joked.

"It's an inspiration!" Coral clapped her hands.

Burt studied her. "You're not serious."

"Why not? It ought to be fun."

"It's a go then. I know a cozy little hotel restaurant just off the boardwalk where you can get good wine and food that's out of this world."

Burt paid the check and they headed down Eighth Avenue to avoid the congestion. He drew her close. Her arm pressed into his side and their thighs brushed in walking.

As they turned in at Forty-second Street for the subway, a sudden gust of wind whipped Coral's scarf over her shoulder.

With his free hand Burt tucked the scarf back around her neck, a queer feeling almost choking him. She was such a kid, he thought for the thousandth time. Leaning there against him, she seemed small and helpless, needing the strength he had forgotten was his.

He tried to swallow the tightness in his throat. He had never felt like this before. Vivien was so capable, so thoroughly competent to handle her own affairs—and his. He had a sense of inadequacy before Vivien that had irritated him, in the beginning. Then he no longer fought it; he accepted its dominion. She made more money in a month than he made in three. Somehow her smartness made him, deep down inside, feel stupid, numb. He had fallen into a rut and had been content to jog along there; but lately he was restless, looking out over the rim of the groove where Vivien's superiority kept him—impatient to crawl out into wider space where he could breathe newness, get that tired and thwarted something that was beginning to nag at him out of his system.

It was odd that with Vivien, it was always she who tucked *his* scarf in, buttoned up his overcoat against the wind as if he were incapable of doing a thing for himself. . . . He remembered how it was, that old football knee of his keeping him out of the army, when he wanted to join the ambulance corps. It was the only time he had ever seen Vivien cry and he had given in to her protests, submitted resignedly to her coddling. . . .

He looked down at the young, lush oval of Coral's cheek beside his shoulder and an unfamiliar consciousness of courage flooded him. He felt knowing, sure, masterful; and at the same time warm and tingling, as if the glow of her youth were contagious. Her want of independence—so vastly unlike Vivien—lent him a feeling of useful power, her freshness gave him a surge of elation. What he experienced was like a feeding of something inside that had been for a long time starving. It was like freedom and fulfillment.

"One thing about Coney," Coral was saying. He could feel the warmth of her arm through his coat sleeve. "Even if the dinner's no good, you can be sure of the soup."

Burt caught on and they both laughed.

"That woman's everywhere—like air. I'm going to look under the table anyway."

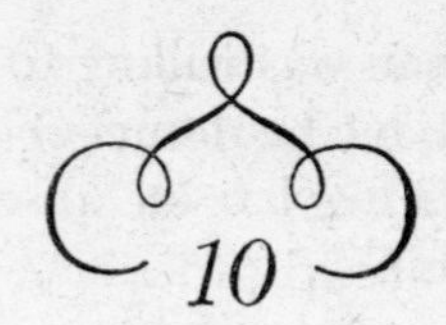

10

MRS. MARSAN knew Burt and Coral had not come in Thanksgiving night. For the following three weeks their comings and goings were unscheduled and rather sketchy. Once Coral called by to borrow a can of milk. "I'm so busy I can't even get over to Brinkmann's," she said. Mrs. Marsan pretended to have to look for the milk while she probed for details. Coral's talk was all about the course and the girls and instructors at the studio and unheard-of things like Row-Ex and Tiger Stretch and Procedure-and-Pace and the Three Quarter Pivot. Mrs. Marsan had to hand over the milk when it fell out of the cupboard into full view. "Well now, don't work yourself to death," she advised drily.

Then Vivien came home from the hospital and Burt's hours became more regular. Mrs. Marsan dropped in to see her on her first day back. Vivien was sitting up in bed cold-creaming her face. She looked every bit as tired as before.

"I was so worried about Burt." She massaged her forehead distractedly. "He hates eating out and with no one to fix things for him I suppose he didn't eat at all. I find him a little nervous and pale."

"Oh, men always manage," Mrs. Marsan said.

'Of course, he's upset too about losing his job."

"Did he? Well, I declare!"

"I can give him money. But he's so sensitive about it. Now he insists on giving me I O U's."

"How did he come to lose it?" Since Vivien seemed communicative, Mrs. Marsan was willing to give her every chance.

"Some argument about his hours. You'd think they would have overlooked his being late or absent a couple of times, with me in the hospital."

"Wouldn't you? A couple of times," Mrs. Marsan agreed.

"I told him—he's sure to land something else. I don't find things so different from last year. You know the watch I gave him for his birthday? He dropped it and they're going to take three months to fix it. Isn't that a scandal?"

"It certainly is!" Her indignation was genuine. So that's how he explained the watch. . . .

"I'm going to miss him." Vivien shoved the cold cream in the drawer where she kept the calendar. "It will be the first Christmas and New Year's we've spent apart since we met."

"Is he going some place?" All this was very interesting.

"He wants to take a run over to Detroit to see his folks. I don't blame him. It's ten years since he's seen them. I'm giving him a new suit and the trip for Christmas."

"Wonder you wouldn't go along."

"I've lost enough time from Marie Louise already. I can't desert her altogether in the middle of the holiday season."

"Too bad you have to break your record—about the first year apart, I mean." I do feel sorry for her. . . .

"Well, it's for the best, I suppose. If we were together I'd just be keeping late hours and running around. I have to put the soft pedal on that kind of thing for a while."

Mrs. Marsan got up to leave. She looked at Vivien and sighed.

It was funny that a woman could be so smart about other things and so woodenly dumb about a man.

2

The weather had changed during the night and by morning everything was under snow. In the downtown New York shopping district the crossings were churned to a dirty brown sherbet and Mrs. Marsan was glad to be getting home with her armful of parcels and Jean.

Snappy Tune was a twenty to one shot that had not come in and Christmas money was produced by a temporary combination of Sobel and Mr. Cernak's opera glasses. Shopping was part of Mrs. Marsan's program for getting Jean over the hurdle of the holidays. "The streets are so bad and I can't carry everything myself," she explained.

Jean came reluctantly. She would have refused if she had had the least hope that her refusal would be accepted. She advanced the weather and other excuses but all were overruled. In the end she went because going promised more peace and privacy than remaining at home.

Mrs. Marsan stood her before show windows and towed her through department stores. Jean stared at everything without interest. Exquisite clothes and shining gifts and good things to eat might have been so much rag and rot for all the impression they made on her. The crowds jostled and pushed her and she gave no sign of caring. She was only as alive as a sleepwalker.

Mrs. Marsan unlocked the door while Jean held most of the bundles and Lady leapt up to her elbow, barking crazily. She had a new sweater for Lady.

"Just put everything on the sofa inside and I'll get some hot coffee made," she said. They had lunched in town and Jean had left half of hers uneaten.

"I can't stay."

"Oh, can't you?"

Jean deposited the packages and fled. Mrs. Marsan felt for

a moment nonplused. The first number on her program had not scored a success. Perhaps she would have better luck with Jean at the show. She had Christmas matinée tickets to the loudest and funniest musical on Broadway.

She unwrapped her purchases and sorted them. Five pounds of pecans. The annual tie for Mr. Cernak. Cigarettes for Coral. A monkey that ran up a pole for Maxie. Microscope for Joey. Fruit cake made with wine for Jessamine. A bottle of brandy for herself, for cold nights at the window when hot coffee alone was not warming enough. She went for a corkscrew and uncorked the brandy and took a jigger. It tasted good. She made room for the bottle in the medicine chest in the bathroom.

Mr. Ingalls was such a nice young man. She wondered if she knew him well enough to remember him with a present? Perhaps not. After all, there seemed to be only one thing Mr. Ingalls really wanted. Adrian Larsch. Well, Lily, maybe it's not impossible to give him Adrian, for a couple of hours anyway. You have to do something about that, you know. Why not have them over for eggnog on Christmas Eve? Along with Jean. That would square things nicely.

Mrs. Marsan waited at the window for Adrian to come home from school. She usually appeared around four—and disappeared before five. Most of the interim was taken up with bathing and dressing. Mrs. Marsan knew because she had already tried to talk to Adrian only to be informed distantly through the door that Adrian was in the tub. The best way to catch her was on the stairs, going or coming.

At four-fifteen Adrian stepped out of the bus and entered the building in more than her customary rush. Mrs. Marsan hurried to the hall. Instead of turning toward her own apartment, abreast Mrs. Marsan's, Adrian steered toward the opposite end and vanished into Joey's.

Mrs. Marsan quickly withdrew. She opened the sack of

pecans and poured three quarters of them into a brown paper bag. She picked up the bag and made for Joey's, Lady at her heels.

Edna was home. She had been given half a day for Christmas shopping which she had already done on Saturday afternoons. It was like Edna to be early and exact. A half-dressed tree stood in the middle of the living room, and Adrian, unnoticing, beside it.

"Well, I can't stop now," Adrian was saying. "Suppose I pass back on my way out. You will have found it by then and I can look over it in the train and between acts."

"It was an envelope as big as a desk blotter. I can't imagine where I put it." Edna was rummaging through wrappings and boxes on the floor. "But in a mess like this you can misplace anything."

"Don't bother. I'll be back."

Adrian was off before Mrs. Marsan could open her mouth.

"The Phantom of the Opera," Joey said from the window.

"Here! Lie down here!" Edna snatched a newspaper from a chair and spread it on the rug for Lady to lie on. Lady cringed before Edna and hid her tail between her legs.

"Lie down, Lady," Mrs. Marsan said. "Would that be what you were looking for?"

"For heaven's sake!" Edna looked flustered and foolish. "Under the newspaper. . . ."

Mrs. Marsan had decided to wait until Adrian came back.

"I brought you some pecans."

"Pecans from The Plantation!" Joey said it in capitals. She sped her wheel chair up to the table. "Turn on the light, Ed." The brown nuts dropped through the fingers of both hands, making a merry clicking sound. "To think! Maybe they're from The Very Tree."

"What tree?" said Edna shortly.

Mrs. Marsan started, "Well, maybe they're not from *that* tree—"

"From The Very Tree in the Pecan Grove where Henry proposed and took her in his arms. That's when her sister saw them and got so jealous and hateful. She was in love with Henry herself."

"It was nice of her not to be too hateful to send the pecans," Edna observed.

"My sister didn't send them." Mrs. Marsan coughed politely behind her hand.

"Of course she didn't!" Joey laughed. "Eloise did. Last year she sent pralines. Eloise is the faithful Old Mammy. She's been in The Family for years. She knows what a hex Mrs. Marsan's sister is and simply dotes on Mrs. Marsan and longs for The Day—"

"Well, the pecans are very nice." Edna cut in with a finality that was intended to put an end to this phase of the conversation.

"Everything is nice on The Plantation," Joey persisted. "The first thing I'm going to do when I get there is mount a horse and ride for miles and miles through the cotton fields."

Edna had been wiring a ball to a lower branch. She stood up and froze.

"Oh, are you?"

"I'm going to have a pet alligator and a kennel full of hound dogs. And possibly a possum and a racoon."

"Did you say plantation or Bronx Park Zoo?" Edna's eyebrows raised and her gray-green eyes turned coldly on Mrs. Marsan. A shiver scraped Mrs. Marsan's spine.

Joey, cracking pecans, paid no attention to Edna.

"I'll have a balcony to my wing at Magnolia Manor and Eloise will come every morning to bring me coffee in bed and in the evening the darkies will play their banjos and sometimes a handsome man like Henry will ride up the river road to have dinner with us."

"Turtle soup and fried chicken and sweet potatoes and molasses pecan pie," Mrs. Marsan listed.

"Of course, Mrs. Marsan's sister will have to die first," Joey sighed.

Mrs. Marsan reassured Joey. "She can't last much longer. At her age and with the Bright's as bad as she's got it—"

"You're counting your chickens before they're hatched." Edna turned again to the tree. "She might leave the place to somebody else."

"But she can't! Can she, Mrs. Marsan? Didn't you tell me she *couldn't?*"

"She sure can't," Mrs. Marsan stated positively. "She worked on my mother to leave her everything, but when *she* dies everything comes to me. That's in the will and you can't change a will unless it's your own."

"You can't be *sure* about a will unless it's your own, either," Edna said, pinching the end of a tinsel star into shape.

Joey sat up straight, suddenly. For the first time there was a serpent in her dream—cold and slimy uncertainty.

A pecan shot out of Joey's hand to the floor and Lady got up from her newspaper to sniff it. Mrs. Marsan picked up the pecan and threw it back into the bag, colliding with Edna's eyes as she resumed her chair. She could read what Edna was thinking as clearly as if Edna's thoughts ran around on the outside of her head in electric lights, like headlines belting the top of the Times Building. *That pecan should have been washed. It was full of germs. It touched the floor and that damned dog put her nose on it. Now I'll have to wash every pecan in the bag.*

"Stop eating pecans, Joey!" Edna said. "It'll spoil your dinner."

"What if it does? If I stop it will spoil my *fun.*"

"That's right," Mrs. Marsan seconded. "Let her have fun. She can always have dinner."

"Don't eat any more, darling," Edna insisted. "For my sake. Will you?"

Joey pushed the bag back sulkily and threw her last picked kernel to Lady.

"Don't—don't—don't. If I *don't* everything how in heaven's name will I ever find out what I can *do?*"

"If I didn't love you better than anything else in the world I wouldn't care what you did." Edna looked at her tenderly.

"Then I wish—" Joey bit the sentence in two and swallowed the rest of it. She tossed her head. Her hands in her lap were clenched and still. "I'm going to have one hell of a good time on The Plantation, all right. I'll even get drunk if I want to! I'll have a better time than Coral Sands."

"Why, Joey! For heaven's *sake!*" Edna jumped to her feet and stood there staring at her unbelieving. "You've never talked like this before. I do everything I can possibly think of to make you happy. I had no idea you weren't." The wound in her voice hardened over. "Of course I can't stay home from work and watch that other people don't inject you full of poisonous piffle!"

Joey flushed.

"I won't have you calling The Plantation piffle, do you hear? *I won't have it!*" Her anger cracked in the middle and she turned miserably to Mrs. Marsan. "Oh, my God. The Seldens must be turning over in their Ancestral Graves."

"That's all right." Mrs. Marsan waved a hand. "That's perfectly all right. The Seldens were always restless, anyhow."

Adrian returned for the envelope. Other women, well-groomed and chicly dressed, might look fresh from the bandbox, but Adrian looked fresh from the atelier of some skillful artist. She had an air of being newly sculptured and polished. Her ivory smooth face topped by hempen hair was like a cameo under her slick black hat. She had on a three-quarter black seal coat over a green wool dress.

"I thought I heard 'a sound of revelry by night,' " she said. "Go right on. Don't mind me. Did you find the envelope?"

Edna was embarrassed. "I didn't know you could hear us in the hall." She cast around for the envelope. It was gone again.

"We were just talking about The Seldens of Mississippi—Mrs. Marsan was *née* Selden—and The Plantation. It's so exciting"—Joey alibied—"I guess you get excited just talking about it."

"It seems to me I had that literature in my hand a minute ago." Distractedly Edna searched behind and under boxes. She moved Lady off with her foot and looked under the newspaper.

Ordinarily Adrian would have glanced at her watch and said she was late already and another minute was too long to wait. But Joey's statement about The Seldens of Mississippi and The Plantation intrigued her.

"Is there a plantation?" she prodded.

"It's Mrs. Marsan's sister's now, but it'll be hers soon."

"You ought to visit Mississippi some day, Miss Larsch," Mrs. Marsan suggested. "Wonderful state."

"I didn't know you were interested in a plantation," Adrian said. "Cane?"

"No, cotton," Joey supplied eagerly. "Did you ever see a cotton field in bloom? Neither have I. But it must be beautiful. They call it Southern snow. Don't they?" She looked at Mrs. Marsan benignly overflowing her chair. "Southern snow—that's how Mrs. Marsan came to tell me about The Plantation. It was snowing like fury that day and I was cold enough to cube because it was a war winter and the coal hadn't come. I had to go to bed to keep warm and I couldn't look out the window and see the kids sledding in the street or snowballing or anything. I was griping all over. I even got mad at God. Then Mrs. Marsan came and she said, 'Some places you can have snow and nice warm weather, too.' And she told me about The Plantation and all the good times you can have down there."

"I'm not having a good time looking for that literature!" Edna sliced impatiently into the talk. "I just had it in my hand—"

"Oh, I have time," Adrian said surprisingly. "I'm not going to Rio tomorrow." She resumed: "I've heard about plantation life. The manor houses with their white columns showing through the oaks and magnolias must be charming."

"They *are!*" Joey beamed. "Magnolia Manor—that's The Selden Seat."

Edna turned around sharply.

"The Selden seat wouldn't be on that envelope, would it?" she inquired, impaling Mrs. Marsan on a look.

Mrs. Marsan got up and giggled.

"Well! What do you know!"

She was not disturbed about the discovery now because she could see that Adrian's interest was already trapped. She would have hated to give up the literature before Adrian was sufficiently impressed; but her luck could hardly have been better. Now she had not only Adrian—for at least the length of the stairs—but Adrian's esteem and unstinted good will.

"I think I'll just walk down to the sidewalk with you." Mrs. Marsan grabbed her advantage. "I have to give Lady a turn anyhow."

"Yes, do," Adrian accepted heartily.

She thanked Edna for the literature. "I'll let you know when I'm ready to book passage."

Edna said all right, any time, and went back to trimming the tree.

Mrs. Marsan wanted to ask Adrian more about the trip but that could wait until later. What mattered now was getting Adrian invited for Christmas Eve, or, much more important, getting her promise she would come. Adrian was in an unheard-of unhurried mood. They went down the stairs together almost leisurely, Lady with her rump up in the air loping ahead.

"I'm having a little eggnog on Christmas Eve. Couldn't you come?"

Adrian actually stopped. She looked down the rest of the stairs and thought hard.

"Christmas Eve. . . . What am I doing Christmas Eve? Oh, yes. *The Cherry Orchard.* No, I couldn't possibly. I'm *so* sorry."

Adrian's regret was not routine; it was genuine. Mrs. Marsan could see it in the disappointed pout of her chiseled mouth, and both marveled and rejoiced.

"How about Christmas night then?" she substituted promptly.

"Christmas night. . . ." Adrian flicked through the pile of dates in her head. "Oh. Lily Pons. *Lucia.*" She made a little "Too bad" sound with her tongue against her teeth.

"Christmas afternoon?" In her emergency Mrs. Marsan forgot about the matinée.

"Oh, dear. The Cloisters. They're having medieval music. And the Middle Ages stained glass windows they took out for safety during the war are going to be back. Mrs. John D. Rockefeller, Jr., is lending two angels from the eleventh, or is it the sixteenth, century. . . ."

Mrs. Marsan was dejected, but not defeated.

"Maybe you could come Christmas morning."

"Eggnog in the *morning?*" Adrian laughed. "That would be somewhat anachronic, wouldn't it? Besides, it would be simply sinful to miss the Christmas morning music at Trinity."

"Well, come any night between now and next year," Mrs. Marsan sighed. She leaned against the bannister, her heart beating uncomfortably. Suppose Adrian was fully engaged right on up to Rio.

Adrian opened her spacious bag and took out a line-a-day diary which she used as a date book. She peeled back one page after the other.

"*Oedipus Rex*—that's a must . . . Wang Yung at the Cherry Lane . . . *Il Barbiere di Siviglia*—I *must* see the Barber . . . Exhibition of Chinese Bronzes . . . Lecture on Islamic Art . . . Handel's *Messiah* . . . Symphony. . . ." She looked up at last. "Well, it looks like the hundred-headed hydra, doesn't it? But—let's see—I have a Marian Anderson concert on December thirtieth, but I could cut out the Prints of the Counter Reformation in the afternoon to be with you. Shall we say, at four?"

Oh, my God! Out of three hundred and sixty-five days in the year, and twenty-four hours in every one of them, why does she have to pick out a time when Mr. Ingalls is chained up checking groceries. . . .

"Four *P.M.?*" Mrs. Marsan stalled.

"Why, P.M. of *course.*" Adrian blinked. "It's a Sunday," she added matter-of-factly.

"It's a *Sunday!*" Mrs. Marsan put her hand to her heart. "Well! That makes all the difference in the world."

"Sunday the thirtieth at four, then." Adrian corrected her calendar with a silver pencil.

"Mr. Cernak and his sister always drop in Sundays at four," Mrs. Marsan remembered, "but you'll like talking to Jessamine. She was a grand opera singer, you know."

"I've tried to speak to her on a number of occasions, but I've never found her lucid," Adrian said.

"But she will be this time, because it's the end of the month."

"Really?" Adrian blinked again.

They continued down the stairs.

"I promised Jean Landry she could come over, too." Mrs. Marsan knew she would have to drag Jean.

Adrian said nothing, but the raising of eyebrows could not have been more actual if they had creaked, and the air around her iced. She pushed the door for Lady, and Mrs. Marsan followed them onto the sidewalk.

"And I've asked Mr. Ingalls."

A rod stiffened in Adrian's back. Turning on Mrs. Marsan she looked fully two feet taller.

"That *pig?*"

"Pig?"

Mrs. Marsan felt weak again. In a minute the bus would come, and Adrian would run for it. It was impossible to think of Adrian and a bus together without picturing her running for it.

"I see you don't know." Adrian fixed her with a level stare. "Has nobody told you he's living with that girl?"

"No," Mrs. Marsan said truthfully, her hand again on her heart.

"Well, it's a fact. Edna Brent's colored maid told me all about it."

"Pearl?"

"I'm sorry, but I can't come if he's going to be there."

"It's an outrageous lie," Mrs. Marsan declared. "There's nothing between them—"

"But the hall."

"It might just as well be the ocean!"

"Well, where there's the smoke of scandal there's usually

the fire of fact." Adrian always improved proverbs. Impatiently she looked up the street for the bus.

"Pearl got them mixed up with somebody else!" Mrs. Marsan said desperately. The lights of the bus were growing specks.

"With whom, pray?" Adrian asked coldly.

"With Mr. Villars and Coral Sands, I guess."

Adrian jumped as if a noise had startled her.

"My *word!*"

"Mr. Ingalls—"

"Well, I'm sorry I misjudged him. Here comes the bus."

"Is it all right to ask him?"

Adrian was running. Her high patent heels clicked on the pavement like hail. On the other side of the street she turned as the bus door folded back, and waved a gloved hand.

"The thirtieth at four!" she called.

Mrs. Marsan leaned against the mailbox and drew a deep breath.

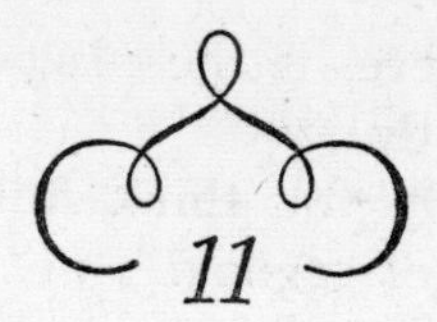

Mr. Ingalls was the first to arrive at the party. He had on a new gray suit meticulously creased and a dark blue brocaded tie, quiet, like himself. His light hair was combed back neatly from his forehead and his gray eyes were eager and expectant behind their glasses.

"Sit down, sit down," Mrs. Marsan waved. "You don't have to jump up every time I do."

"Let me help with something," Mr. Ingalls said.

"Everything's fixed. Only I wanted to make sure the cake was *covered.*" She came back from the kitchen. "On account of the uninvited, you know. I'd put borax and sugar down if Lady didn't like it better than they do."

"Now don't wear yourself out," Mr. Ingalls ordered. "Sit down yourself and catch your breath. Here, let me take that."

He relieved her of a bowl in which gladioli were spread out like the ribs in a fan.

"If I didn't have that frog to stick them on they'd never stand up." She leaned back, short-winded, in a corner of the sofa. "Don't they look nice?"

"I wanted to bring roses, but there weren't any," Mr. Ingalls regretted. "Where shall I put them?"

"Right here." She wagged a finger at the bridge table before the sofa.

"Wouldn't they be better somewhere else?" Mr. Ingalls urged.

"No. I want them to be an epilogue."

"The center, I believe, is the place for an epergne." He stressed the word slightly.

"Yes, the center. Do you think Adrian will notice we're having coffee instead of eggnog?"

"She may notice it, but she won't mind, I'm sure."

"I couldn't, you see, on account of Jessamine. It's the end of the month and Mr. Cernak says the taste would torture her. When she's without, merely the smell makes her scream."

Mr. Ingalls sat down on the sofa.

"Did Miss Larsch seem—glad to come?"

"Well, it was a job settling on the date. I never heard of such hopping around. I couldn't make head or tail of it. I don't remember what it was on Christmas Eve, but on Christmas Day she had to go somewhere to look at some old windows. Windows on Christmas Day! Imagine."

"She's wonderful. . . ." Mr. Ingalls mused.

"Then there was something about the Rockefeller angels, and something else about eggnog being chronic on Christmas morning. Then she had to go see some kind of wrecks. Then she had to go to the barber. What a woman!"

"Did she—" Mr. Ingalls leaned forward—"pass up another engagement to come here this afternoon?"

"She cut out some prince of the Reformation, as far as I could make out."

He settled back again and smiled.

"She has everything," he said happily. "Absolutely everything."

Mrs. Marsan had decided that Jean was to pour. Filling cups and adding cream would lend her a kind of animation, and she would be forced to say at least "Will you pass your cup?" and "One or two?"

Besides, Mrs. Marsan was not capable of doing these things herself because she was wearing corsets. The effort of raising an arm put her completely out of breath. She laced tightly, bringing her bosom up into a broad crêpey plateau in which the cleft showed like a gorge. She had modestly filled in part of the gorge with the costume pin Joey gave her for Christmas. Pearl had selected it—a bright metallic squirrel with a green eye and a jewel-studded tail obviously confused with a peacock's.

Mrs. Marsan was concerned about Jean. It would never do to have to coax her over after Adrian arrived when she had said Jean begged to come. Of course, Jessamine would look lovely pouring, but Mrs. Marsan knew how steady Jessamine's hands were at the end of the month. *Speaking of hands, it's a shame you can't do the pouring yourself, Lily. That Fatal Apple manicure Elvira gave you is practically wasted. But not the double rinse and the Duchess hairdo!* . . . Mrs. Marsan defied anybody not to notice *that.*

The Cernaks arrived. Jessamine was wearing her mauve, the usual green veil tied frothily about her throat. Mr. Cernak had a poinsettia in his buttonhole.

"We'd better be calling Jean," Mrs. Marsan worried. "Mr. Ingalls, go in the bedroom and knock on the wall, will you?"

She had to coach Jean about the cups. The chipped ones for herself and the Cernaks because they were used to them. The side of the sugar bowl *without* the ear to be kept *away* from Adrian. Thank God things came in sets of six. Except the napkins. They had come in a foolish four. Jean was to keep the odd pair on the bottom for Mrs. Marsan and herself. And the table did look thrilling. The pink-iced angel's food there and the peppermint-frosted devil's food here and the frogged flowers in the middle. . . .

"Go knock again, will you, Mr. Ingalls?" Mrs. Marsan would have gone to get Jean herself if Adrian had not been expected any minute. "And tell her to be *sure* to wear that electric blue Vivien gave her with the magenta belt. Just put your mouth to the wall and yell."

Mr. Ingalls drummed on the wall with both fists and relayed the message about the magenta. Then he drummed on the wall again. A resigned "All right" finally sounded from the other side.

He came back into the living room rubbing his hands, which stung a little. "She'll be right over, in her electric," he said.

And then he saw Adrian. He had not heard her come in—naturally. She wavered before him, like a reflection seen in rippling water. He wondered miserably what she thought of the fanfare that must have met her entrance. The gallant greeting he had planned, indeed, rehearsed, was garbled in a blush.

They sat down and Mrs. Marsan saw at once that the seating was wrong but it was too late to do anything about it. As intended, Adrian took the tapestried (borrowed from Jean) at the right of Mrs. Marsan, on the sofa. Since The Correct Thing column in the newspaper said the guest of honor should always be seated at the hostess' right, this was the correct thing. But Mrs. Marsan had not intended that Mr. Cernak should take his chair as usual. She wanted Mr. Ingalls to have it, to be next to Miss Larsch. Jessamine sat next to Mr. Cernak in the overstuffed, and the straight-back armless (from the bedroom) facing Adrian through the gladioli fell to Mr. Ingalls.

"I've been to the most fascinating display of English needlework of the eighteenth century," Adrian said, draping her seal over the back of her chair. Mr. Ingalls jumped to help but Mr. Cernak was closer. "There were a number of rare embroideries from Hardwicke Hall and Hatfield House, and Queen Mary lent a beautiful coverlet from Marlborough."

Mrs. Marsan feared the coffee would cool. She looked over the gladioli toward Mr. Ingalls.

"Would you just go bang again?"

Mr. Ingalls was too interested in needlework to notice.

"There were some reproductions for sale and I bought one." Adrian went into her bag. "This is a copy of an antimacassar from the Victoria and Albert Museum. Isn't it exquisite?" She held it up to view.

"What did you say it was?" Mrs. Marsan asked.

"An antimacassar. I think the etymology of the word is delightful. *Anti* plus *macassar,* oil. In other words, a covering to prevent soiling the backs of chairs by contact with the hair."

"We call it doily," Mrs. Marsan said. "But the whatchamay-call-it is the same, I guess. Doily, oily."

Jean appeared at last. English embroidery and etymology were dropped. Adrian measured her, appraising and approving. Vivien's electric blue with the magenta belt was stunning on Jean with her straight, long tawny hair. Everybody saw she was beautiful except Mr. Ingalls.

Mrs. Marsan beckoned Jean to her side on the sofa, behind the coffee service. She was completely happy now.

"You may begin to pour, dear," she nodded.

It was a pity Society Notes would miss such a newsy item. Mrs. Lily Marsan, *née* Selden, in an autumn brown hostess gown trimmed with cream lace set off by a studded squirrel . . . Mrs. Jean Wilkes Landry, utterly electric in magenta and breath-taking blue, poured . . . A lovely ep—well, bunch —of gladiolas presented Mrs. Marsan by Mr. John Ingalls, manager of the local A&P . . . and Madame Jessamine Cernak, lately of the (what was that opera company?) in Milan . . . Miss Adrian Larsch, lovely in a lavender two-piece fresh from the fingers of Lilly Daché (or did she make hats?) and a queer high-peaked purple velour piece of headgear (hats get crazier and crazier) reported on Queen Mary's lovely bedspread. . . .

Jean poured very nicely. She knew exactly what to do.

Oh, my God! Adrian got one of the chipped cups.

"Imagine that!" Mrs. Marsan would have swapped with her but she was not sure it was The Correct Thing. "In all the years and years and *years* I've had this set I never noticed before that cup was chipped."

Adrian looked at the cup with quickened interest.

"Have you had it so long?"

"Oh, for ages. Here, let me change with you. I haven't touched this."

"Nonsense," Adrian said. "I adore old china that's been in the family for generations. Haviland, is it?"

"Hand-painted," Mrs. Marsan supplemented.

"Chaplet, Delaplanche, or Damousse?"

"Hum?" inquired Mrs. Marsan.

Adrian raised the cup and critically regarded the bottom. A look of horror crossed her face. Then a vertical equals sign appeared sharply between her eyes, and for some moments she was busily silent, her lips pressed together.

Suddenly she gave Mrs. Marsan a queer speculative side glance and remarked as if she were thinking out loud: "It strikes me as so strange that you speak without any trace of a Southern accent. . . ."

"Oh, that." Mrs. Marsan waved a scornful hand. "I got rid of it after coming to New York. You lose it after living North for a long time, you know."

"Do you have any other souvenirs of the plantation," Adrian asked pointedly, "that the years haven't worn away—or chipped?"

Mrs. Marsan considered for a minute. "I don't believe I have."

"Yes, you have." Mr. Cernak looked stern. "A monthly tribute, Mrs. Marsan, soaked in the sweat of your slaves."

Mrs. Marsan thought it bad taste to speak of sweat while people were eating and drinking. She ignored Mr. Cernak and fed devil's food to Lady, washed and combed and wearing a blue satin ribbon around her neck. Adrian leaned back in her chair, withdrawn in thought, a slight and oddly satisfied smile twisting her lips.

"Go on, Mr. Cernak," Mr. Ingalls laughed. "Slavery was abolished years ago."

"Was it?" Mr. Cernak put his cup down. "*Was* it? What am I? What are you?" He moved restlessly in his chair and the arm came off as always, thudding the floor. He picked it up and used it as a baton to emphasize what he had to say. "Listen. Don't you know we are living today in a cancerous condition of physical and moral serfdom? Compare the twentieth century with the tenth. What do you find? The same unfair feudalistic setup exactly! Who are your barons? Who are your lords? Your bankers and manufacturers. Your—" he pointed the arm at Mrs. Marsan across the table—"land-owners and office-holders. Who do you depend on for your miserable pittance of food and shelter and false security? On them. Are you getting it for nothing? No. No more now than in the Middle Ages. What are you paying for it? Blood, brains, and liberty. And you say slavery is *abolished?*" Mr. Cernak brought the arm down on the table and the china rattled. "No, sir, it isn't!"

"Perhaps a return to the Middle Ages wouldn't be so bad." Adrian, coming out of her detachment, sipped her coffee coolly. "If our time could produce just one piece of architecture as fine as the Chapter House from the Abbey of Notre-Dame-de-Pontaut that I saw up at the Cloisters the other day, or the arcade and garth of Saint-Michel-de-Cuxa, we'd have enough cause for pride."

"If our time could produce the four-hour working day and the four-day week"—Mr. Cernak tapped the table—"we'd have as fine as that and finer. We might even have a Michelangelo."

"Michelangelo was Renaissance," Adrian said stiffly. "We were speaking of the Middle Ages."

"I don't believe holding a full-time job can keep a man back from anything." Mr. Ingalls frowned into his cup. "If he's got it in him, it will come out, somehow. . . ."

"Of course it will," Mrs. Marsan agreed promptly. "Like measles. I remember—"

"I think," Adrian continued, "that a standardization of society and a leveling of income would crush out The Finer Things of Life. Art, literature, and music are born of struggle, not killed by it."

"What about improved working conditions for the laboring masses? Higher wages? Better education? More leisure? Decent housing? Medical care? Social security?" Mr. Cernak shook the arm at Adrian. "Don't they have anything to do with the finer things of life?"

Mr. Ingalls was distressed. He wished Mr. Cernak would stop aiming that thing at Adrian. He wished he could think of something to say to detour the conversation, instead of sitting there on the edge of the chair like a tongue-tied oaf. Something graceful and gay, that would make everybody laugh and clear the air. Something that would melt Adrian and make her smile and at the same time cool Mr. Cernak off and make him still.

"I'm not interested in Marx," Adrian said from a height.

"I'm not interested in Marx either!" Mr. Cernak declared. "I'm only interested in *men!*"

"Oh, come now," Mrs. Marsan cajoled. "Miss Larsch is only interested in men, too. Aren't you, dear?"

"*This devil cake is delicious!*" Mr. Ingalls shouted.

They all looked startled and Jessamine jumped. The coffee plashed over the rim of her cup and onto the saucer. Lady, on the sofa between Mrs. Marsan and Jean, threw back her head and barked sharply.

Mrs. Marsan remembered The Correct Thing from the daily column. The hostess should appear smilingly unconcerned over slight accidents at the table. . . . She turned beaming to Adrian, as if nothing had happened.

"Dear, how did you find the Rockefeller angels?"

"They were polychromes," Adrian said.

"Did you—see angels?" Jessamine's voice trembled like her hands.

"She saw the opera, too." At last the talk was sensible. Mr. Cernak was engaged in getting the arm back on the chair. He was a little man again with watery blue eyes and thin gray fingers of hair aslant his forehead. It was strange how big he got when he was full of words, and how he shrank as soon as they were out of him. "She saw—what was it you saw, dear?"

"Lily Pons. *Lucia.*"

"I know," Jessamine said softly.

"I thought she surpassed herself in the 'Regnava nel Silenzio.' "

Jessamine hummed, threading a few words here and there like beads on a vibrating string.

"Why, that's beautiful!" Adrian said, amazed.

"No, it's not!" Jessamine contradicted. "It's ugly. It's utterly ugly. It should be as clear and sweet as water. And it's mud and manure."

"*I* think it's fine, too, Miss Cernak," Mr. Ingalls said sincerely.

"No," Jessamine insisted. "That was twenty years ago. Then everything was beautiful. Then everything was fine."

"Don't think about it, Jessie." All the fire had left Mr.

Cernak. He looked cold and ashen. "Talk about something else, Jessie."

Adrian ignored him. "What about twenty years ago?"

"I could sing," Jessamine said. "I could sing so that kings and queens listened to me. Do you know what it is to sing?" Her great blue eyes blazed around the circle. "It is like speaking to God. It is telling Him for humanity all that they cannot express themselves in their prayers. Singing is the articulate soul." She clamped her large white hands on the table and now the table trembled. "Do you know what it is not to be articulate?"

Mr. Ingalls swallowed hard. "You mean—to want to say something, and to feel you can't, exactly, and to strive and struggle with words as if they were monsters—"

Jessamine gave no sign of hearing. She clutched her throat under the billowy green veil. "To be stopped up, here?" she demanded. "*Do you know?*"

"I don't understand," Adrian said, troubled.

"At first it was only as big as a bee, stinging me all the time. . . . Then it grew to be a big green snake, with a swollen head like a cobra, strangling me"—Jessamine's voice rose—"*strangling me!*—"

"Stop, Jessie." Mr. Cernak put his hand on her arm. "Jessie—"

"—strangling me so I couldn't sing! As big and green and long as this scarf—" She stood up. Her shaking fingers tangled in the scarf, tearing at it. She untied it finally and snatched it off, leaning over toward Adrian. "It left its fangs. Look—you can see—"

"It hardly shows," Mrs. Marsan said. "I've told her a hundred times—if I didn't *know*, I wouldn't even notice it."

"It left its fangs." Nervously Jessamine veiled her throat again. "After, when I sang, there was no purity. It was only the poison that poured out."

"My cousin Hattie had her goiter out," Mrs. Marsan said, "and it didn't hurt her voice at all. But of course, she wasn't a singer."

"Oh," Adrian said.

"Sit down, Jessie," Mr. Cernak pleaded. "Try not to think of all that."

"Didn't you sing at all afterward?" Adrian asked.

"*I* sang. Jessamine Cernak did not sing. Do you think a soprano like Cernak would sing in second-rate stock after Milan, Moscow, Paris, London, Berlin, Vienna? Tell me. Do you?"

"You're every bit as good as anything I hear on Joey Brent's radio," Mrs. Marsan asserted.

"Do you know what critics are? Ghouls. Vampires. Do you know what they said? 'The only great Cernak died on the operating table.' Who am I? What am I? Nothing!"

"Look out for the frog, dear." Mrs. Marsan steadied the flowers and Jessamine stared at them in terror.

"Jessie." Mr. Cernak got up and pulled her back into her chair. "Drink your coffee, Jessie."

"And have another piece of cake." Mrs. Marsan knew how Jessamine craved sweets at the end of the month. "Pass your plate, dear. Shall Jean give you devil's or angel's?"

Jessamine quaked with a vast shudder. She pressed her hands against her eyes. "I won't look at them," she mumbled. "I won't look." She got up abruptly and fled from the room. A moment later Mrs. Marsan heard the bathroom door slam.

"I must ask you to excuse Jessamine." Worry showed through Mr. Cernak's dignity. "She hasn't slept for several nights."

"You see, she's always like that when she's been without," Mrs. Marsan explained to the others.

"We—understand thoroughly." Mr. Ingalls sounded husky. He cleared his throat.

The hostess should appear smilingly. . . .

"I'm so glad you worship music." Mrs. Marsan smiled on Adrian as the midday sun. If only she could interest Adrian in Jean sufficiently to take her out sometimes. "Jean is fond of it, too. She went with me to a musical the other day."

"I like music, but I don't waste my time on musicals," Adrian said.

"Perhaps it was a *musicale?*" Mr. Ingalls suggested.

Mrs. Marsan made it clear. "It was one of those Broadway shows."

There was a silence, during which Mrs. Marsan tried to figure out the difference between music and musicals. She gave it up. After all, this party was gotten up to get Adrian and Mr. Ingalls together, and she ought to concentrate on that. Let's see. Adrian was very much impressed with the plantation, and didn't Mr. Ingalls say his father had a farm?

"Yes, country life is wonderful!" She noticed how Adrian's eyes opened with a start. "You ought to get Mr. Ingalls to tell you about his father's place."

"I'd like to very much," Mr. Ingalls said eagerly. "It isn't exciting, but if you've always lived in a city you might find it interesting."

"Were *you* raised on a plantation?" Adrian sat up very straight trying to see him over the gladioli.

"Well, in Nebraska we call it a farm." Confound those gladioli— It was like talking through a picket fence—

"Oh, a *farm.*" Adrian sank back, disappointed.

"Within a few hours of Lincoln. You've heard of Lincoln?" It was swell, talking to Adrian like this about home.

"Not the town." She shrugged.

It was obvious that Adrian was becoming bored. Mr. Ingalls clutched frantically for some topic that would hold her attention, something about which he could speak with force and even erudition. He knew next to nothing about medieval art. Time for that—some day—

"Miss Larsch, did you ever hear about Manuel Lisa?" He sat on the edge of his chair, gripping the sides with both hands.

"Don't you mean *Mona* Lisa?"

"No." A red agony came into his face. "He was the first white settler in Nebraska. Miss Larsch, are you interested in fur trading?"

"Fur trading!" Adrian recoiled. "Certainly not!"

"I had an uncle who was right smart at horse trading," Mrs. Marsan contributed. "Do you like the horses, dear?"

"I like Rosa Bonheur's."

"Does she have a stable in Florida?"

"She had a studio in Paris," Adrian said impatiently. "She *painted.*"

Adrian rose. She was sorry, she would have to go. She thanked Mrs. Marsan for a pleasant afternoon. Mrs. Marsan did not prevail on her to stay. The effort of conversing, in corsets, with Adrian was beginning to weary her. She struggled foggily with the subtle distinction between farm and plantation, stable horses and studio horses, music and musicals. She longed to unlace and relax.

Mr. Cernak said he would call Jessamine. Adrian begged him not to bother. No, Mr. Cernak insisted, she was gone a long time, and he was uneasy about her. He went to the bathroom.

All except Jean rushed after him when they heard Jessamine's long low cry. Mrs. Marsan could hardly believe her eyes when she saw Jessamine, stretched out stiff in the dry bathtub, fully clothed even to her veil, her feet propped up on the double faucets. Large and beautiful she lay there, like some wax figure taken from a museum. Mrs. Marsan would have thought her dead except for her weird cries whenever Mr. Cernak tried vainly to get her up.

Mrs. Marsan stifled a small scream. On the floor beside the tub rolled an empty bottle. The mirrored door to the medicine cabinet was wide open and a large space gaped where the bottle had been. It was Mrs. Marsan's Christmas brandy.

"She's out," Mr. Cernak said quietly.

"Is there anything we can do?" Concern and sympathy looked from behind Mr. Ingalls' glasses.

"Nothing." Mr. Cernak shook his head. "Just let her sleep. She'll come to in a couple of hours."

Mrs. Marsan got a pillow from her bed and a blanket. Mr. Ingalls put the pillow gently under Jessamine's head and spread the blanket over her, tucking it around her broad shoulders.

"I really must go," Adrian's voice broke the stillness like a flute in a mountain pass, "else I'll be deplorably late for my concert."

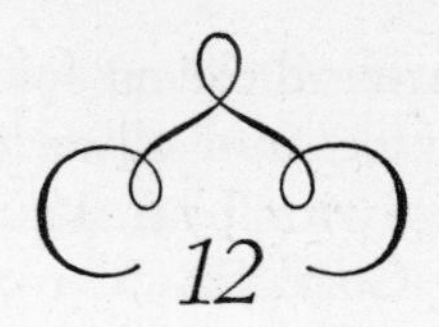

12

New Year's Eve was wet and dirty. The temperature rose so that what might have been snow was rain, and what was rain became a slow trickle, turning the remnants of a white Christmas into sloppy puddles. Later in the evening the sky cleared and the stars came out, but a brisk wind blew and the streets were cold and clammy.

Mrs. Marsan had schemed to have Jean see the New Year in at Times Square and Broadway. "People," Dr. Crowell said. "Activity. Laughter. Life." New Year's Eve in Times Square filled the prescription. It was a long time since Mrs. Marsan had seen the numerals of the old year, in bright lights atop the Times Building, shatter and sink on the stroke of midnight and the new year rise in its stead, dramatic and dazzling. The noise and the surging mob were no longer for her. They left her battling for breath. She preferred to sit comfortably by her window, her cup of coffee before her on the sill, Lady in her lap, watching things that went on behind the tavern through Mr. Cernak's opera glasses.

She had intended saying, "It's a long time since I've seen the fun. Who knows if I'll be here to see it next year? And I need somebody to go with me." But Jean was threatened with a cold. She had a sore throat and was sneezing. Such weather as there was could only make it worse.

Early in the afternoon Mrs. Marsan borrowed Joey Brent's domino set. She knew Jean would not be able to sleep. She could hear her walking around next door when she put her good ear to the wall. Around eleven o'clock she had gone over, taking Lady, the dominoes and a bowl of hot floating island.

Now she sat playing with Jean, Lady lying with her nose between her paws on Coral Sands' rug. It was quite homey in Jean's living room. The Brinkmann floor lamp glowed warm and golden under its new Woolworthian shade. The Larsch pictures looked nice on the walls, though Mrs. Marsan cared least for the ballet dancers by Degas since their legs were too lumpy and they were only in black and white. If she had her way, she would have gotten a box of crayons and filled the poor empty things in with some color. Elvira's rubber plant was growing like magic.

"I haven't got a five," Jean said. She looked pretty in Vivien's abandoned jade flannel robe.

"Then you go to the boneyard and pick till you get one," Mrs. Marsan ordered. "Go on. Pick."

While Jean was picking, Mrs. Marsan's eyes fell on the tapestried chair. The upholsterer had done a good job of it. The restoration was Mrs. Marsan's Christmas present to Jean. Cretonne could cover but not keep in the ruptured entrails of the Sig and Hannah chair; clots of cotton fell wherever the chair stood. Now, trussed up and tacked, it was more than presentable; it was imposing.

There was something poetic about Adrian Larsch sitting in that chair yesterday facing Mr. Ingalls, with Mr. Cernak mixed up in the middle—as before. That chair was the brief successor of the sidewalk freak Adrian wanted to write Mr. Kennedy letters about. She would have opposed it more than the wreck of the rocker Duffy and his gang burned because Mr. Ingalls promised her she would never have to look at it again. And there she was sitting in it like a queen—

"You put a six on a seven," Jean said listlessly.

"I was thinking about poetry," Mrs. Marsan apologized. "I guess it don't mix with dominoes."

Mrs. Marsan felt vaguely she had made the wrong move in mentioning Mr. Ingalls' father's farm. She blamed herself. Yet how was she to know that cotton was so far superior to cabbage in Adrian's estimation? Maybe she should have guessed. Where was her head, for heaven's sake? She knew well enough the peculiar power of a plantation to stir interest. She could see her personal stock going up like an elevator, picking up people at every floor, ever since the day Joey, via Pearl, broadcast Mrs. Marsan was part-madam of Magnolia Manor. Adrian found out only recently because she was always in such a rush, nothing could catch up with her, not even news.

"Push the boneyard over, dear. I need a three."

Mr. Cernak was the only one not pleased with the plantation. And wasn't he? Look at all the fun he had fussing about it. Mr. Cernak enjoyed the plantation like everybody else. Maybe not *like*, but *as much as*, anyway. It would be a shame if Mr. Cernak didn't have the plantation to rave over —in a different way from Joey, of course. . . .

"Do you think there aren't any three's left? You've been picking a long time."

"Was I picking for a three? Well, here. I must have found it. A double."

Jean went picking in the boneyard for a three.

A farm was not as fancy as a plantation. She could see it now. Like a ranch and a dairy. Cattle, yes. But did you ever read of rich women going to dairies to wait for a divorce? They went to ranches.

"It's your turn," Jean said.

After all, it was a good deal Mr. Ingalls' own fault. He could have called it his father's place in the country instead of a farm. If Mrs. Marsan didn't know what a gem of a jack-o'-lantern he could make she would say he had no imagination. You can't live without imagination any more than you can live without clothes. The truth is so naked; people will look at it, all right, the way they'll look at anything naked. But are they eager to walk down the street with it or sit across from it at dinner?

It was too bad Adrian had to come back looking for Queen Mary's—or was it King Albert's—antimacassar when Mr. Ingalls was helping clear the table and worse that Lady was lying on the thing. Mr. Ingalls didn't appear to advantage. Neither did the antimacassar. Adrian was too sweet not to be upset. "Don't bother," she said when he tried to dust it off. "It's so unimportant. . . ."

Perhaps Mr. Ingalls was fated to be unlucky in love. There was a saying about that. Unlucky in love, lucky at— Mr. Ingalls might have more luck with horses than women. The lady for him might be Lady Luck herself.

"Wait a minute. I have to pick the bones, dear."

Mrs. Marsan found a match and joined it to the stem. She glanced at the clock, Coral's winnings at a Coney Island booth. It was a quarter of twelve. Time was whittling the last seconds off the old year, letting them fall in the silence tiny and quick. It was warm in the room but Mrs. Marsan shuddered, she could not have said why.

The bell rang. Both she and Jean jumped and Lady ran around and barked.

It was Mr. Brinkmann. He had two letters which the postman had left with his mail by mistake. One for Jean, one for Mrs. Marsan. It was a new mailman, Mr. Brinkmann said, put on the route to help out with the holiday rush, and he was like crazy because he had so much to deliver and didn't know the neighborhood.

"I should of brought them sooner, but *Donner!* what a business! I'm crazier than the mailman."

Mrs. Marsan had a note from Coral Sands. She wanted

Mrs. Marsan to take her laundry when it came. "The last time I was out of town I was out forty-five dollars too. The dimwit didn't leave it and he lost it. And these are some of my best things that I can't replace. I won't be home for a week or ten days yet." She had enclosed five dollars and scrawled a P.S. "I have a dancing engagement at a hotel here." There was no heading to the note and Mrs. Marsan looked on the envelope to see the postmark. Atlantic City. A dancing engagement at a hotel. . . . Mrs. Marsan slipped the note back, her eyes narrowed and knowing. "Detroit," Vivien had said.

Mr. Brinkmann extended a fat hand smelling of dill and wished them heartily health and prosperity. In the hall he stopped before Mr. Ingalls' door, where the light fanning over the sill as always announced that Mr. Ingalls was in and up, and called "Happy New Year!" If Mr. Brinkmann recognized the fact that Mr. Ingalls was his most fearsome competitor, he did not dwell on it.

Jean was standing by the lamp with her letter in her hand, mildly puzzled.

"From your sister, I bet," Mrs. Marsan said.

"No, I don't think so."

"You promised to write her and tell her you're all right and where you are. Didn't you?"

"Yes. But I asked her not to write back—for a while."

"Such doings." Mrs. Marsan shook her head. "Well, go on, dear. Open your letter and read it. I'll excuse you."

"No. It can wait."

It was a funny-looking letter in a buff envelope. Mrs. Marsan strained her eyes and craned her neck at it. No stamp. Just a queer kind of postmark. A white strip was pasted along one edge with crowns on it and something printed. She forced herself to make it out. "In His Majesty's Service."

In His Majesty's Service!

"You better read it, dear! Don't you think?"

"Some other time will do." Jean thrust the letter into the pocket of her robe.

Far-sounding from the river a foghorn blew. Boats joined in the deep bellowing. Then auto horns began to bark in the street. Whistles screamed, and what might have been Duffy and his gang tore past, beating on tin pans and dragging clanking chains. The juke box over at the tavern roared and the hubbub of laughter and voices came even through closed windows.

Above the noise and the shouting rose Mr. Brinkmann's greetings as he passed back to his shop.

"Happy New Year! Happy New Year!"

Part II

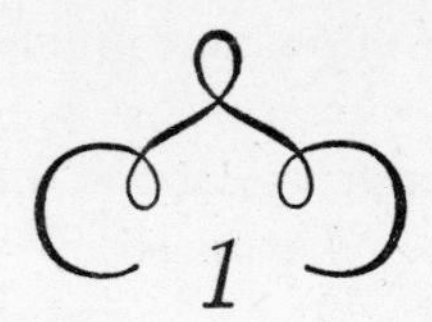

THE FIRST raw days of January tempered, merging into a surprise of mild weather. It was as if spring had missed a cue and made a false entrance. Every morning the sun was as warm as a stove, thawing out the last stubborn patches of ice that returned during the night. Mrs. Marsan saw by the paper that it was the warmest January on record in forty years.

She found Joey sitting by the open window, a cardigan thrown over her shoulders. Mr. Cernak's opera glasses, redeemed a few days before from Sobel, were lying idle in her lap. She was looking at space.

"I see you're like every other kid," Mrs. Marsan chaffed. "Like the old toy best."

"She like the microscope best," Pearl said. "But Miss Edna, *she* don't."

A double darkness showed in Pearl's face, like rain clouds in a midnight sky. Her lower lip jutted out so that the wet purple-pink inside showed. She was perspiring, and the artificial pansies she was wearing today had slipped from the top of her head over her ear. She glowered at the disorder of the living room, the console ransacked and every book taken from the corner shelves and dumped on the floor.

"Not behind the books and not in none of the vases. Nowhere in the kitchen nor bedroom nor bathroom nor closets neither. She must of flushed it down the toilet."

"Never mind looking any more, Pearl." Joey stretched her

face toward the open window and smelled at the sun-drenched air.

"Sig's giving us too much heat for this freak touch of Florida we're having." Mrs. Marsan could feel the blood rushing to her head. She sat down, breathing in staccato jerks. "What're you looking for? Edna lost something again?"

"She hid it." Joey's lips were tight.

"What, for heaven's sake?"

"My microscope."

"It'll take another microscope to find it," Pearl mumbled.

"What did she do that for?"

Joey swallowed, staring over the roof tops. "I don't know."

"*I* know," Pearl said. "Because you got all upset from it yesterday and couldn't eat your dinner."

"I wasn't upset from the microscope. I was upset from what I saw under it."

"What did you see under it?" Mrs. Marsan asked.

"A dead one," Pearl supplied. "Stark, stone dead." She pantomimed Edna putting down borax and sugar.

"I wouldn't feel like eating after that, either," Mrs. Marsan said. "Why don't you just look at nice things, like the minerals that came with the set?"

"I want to look at *real* things, not alone nice things."

"That spot of sink water we looked at the other day after washing the vegetables was nice," Pearl sneered. "Jeez! Lucky we wash them."

"That was the world," Joey said. "I read some place: you can see the world in a drop of water."

"That not *my* idea of seeing the world!"

"Edna was glad enough for you to have the microscope in the beginning," Mrs. Marsan remembered. "She even went out and got in a dishpan of snow for you to look at the snow crystals. I'd no idea myself they were like beautiful flowers."

"That's *Edna's* idea of seeing the world—for *me!*" Joey flushed.

"Where *is* Edna?" Mrs. Marsan asked. "Working this Saturday afternoon?"

"No. She's going all the way down to Chinatown to get me lichee nuts. Somebody told her some place in Pell Street had them."

"Well, she'll walk her legs off and look herself blind to find them for you."

"I know," Joey said quietly.

Since Edna would be late getting home, Mrs. Marsan suggested reading a chapter or two in *Tess*. She went back to her apartment to get the book. It was in the top dresser drawer with her handkerchiefs and a pool of rayon stockings. Since the holidays another book had come to rest in the drawer. It was *An Intelligent Woman's Guide to Socialism and Capitalism,* Mr. Cernak's Christmas gift. The *Guide* was assured of a long rest for Mrs. Marsan disappointedly did not care for it. There were no people in it, no plot, no passion.

Tess looked worn and limp beside the new volume in its bright dust jacket. The coffee spots on the faded cover reproved Mrs. Marsan glumly. Dr. Crowell said she must positively stop drinking so much coffee. It was a pity that all the most alluring pleasures in life were either harmful, forbidden or foolish. Yet otherwise, Mrs. Marsan figured, there would be nothing to distinguish them from commonplace pleasures. She removed the dust jacket from the *Guide* and put it on *Tess,* covering the reproachful coffee stains out of sight.

"Get up, Lady," she said. "You can come along." For several days Lady had been sluggish and lazy. She rose from Mrs. Marsan's bed reluctantly.

Pearl was massaging her face with an ice cube wrapped in a

piece of cheesecloth. "All that sweat pumping out stretch the pores and coarsen the skin," she said. She had covered the traces of rummaging and tidied the room. The pansies were replaced exactly in her shiny, straightened hair.

Mrs. Marsan settled back in her chair and opened the book where a pencil lay between the pages.

"I remember where we were," Joey said, wheeling in from the window. "After Tess's baby died she went to work at Mr. Crick's dairy near Dorchester. Angel Clare, the minister's son, is there studying to be a farmer and he falls in love with her."

"The pencil is at 'Phase the Fifth, The Woman Pays,' but I knew we didn't get that far." Mrs. Marsan turned back the pages.

"The poor little dead bastard," Joey mused. "I don't see how it would have hurt the story any to let it live."

Pearl stopped icing her face. Her angular shoulders crawled in a shudder. "Talk today about nothing but dead," she muttered. "That's a bad sign to start off a new year."

"Sit down and be quiet, Pearl," Joey explained to Mrs. Marsan: "Pearl's nerves are all knotted up."

Pearl sat down, and drawing a file out of her apron pocket, began shaping her fingernails.

"It's about Bernie," Joey went on. "He's been going with her for six weeks and he hasn't propositioned her yet. She thought he'd make a New Year's resolution to do it but it looks as if he's made one not to. It's just soured her soul."

"He make me sick." Pearl attacked her thumb. "Talk to *him* about sweeping a woman off her feet, and he reach for a broom."

"Resolutions are only made to break, anyhow," Mrs. Marsan said. "If he's resolved not to, he will. Here—I have the place."

Mrs. Marsan read on.

" 'Many besides Angel have learnt that the magnitude of lives is not as to their external displacements, but as to their subjective experiences. The impressionable peasant leads a larger, fuller, more dramatic life than the—' " Mrs. Marsan hesitated. She brought the book up to her nose and painfully studied one spot on the page. Clearing her throat, she continued: " '—than the pachydermatous' "—she cleared her throat again—" 'king. Looking at it thus, he found that life was to be seen of the same magnitude here as elsewhere.' "

"That's wonderful." Joey's eyes glowed. "I mean, about the magnitude of lives. Mark that paragraph, will you, Mrs. Marsan? Mark it with double lines in the margins on both sides."

Mrs. Marsan took the pencil and fenced in the part Joey liked.

"That a wonderful king in that paragraph, too," Pearl said. "What kind of a king does it say is he?"

"I said it once," Mrs. Marsan resisted. "That's enough."

Joey frowned. "Pachydermatous. . . . Get the dictionary, Pearl."

Pearl brought her the dictionary and together they searched for the word without success.

"Oh, well. It doesn't matter." Joey gave it up.

" 'Tess,' " Mrs. Marsan continued, " 'was no insignificant creature to toy with and dismiss; but a woman living her precious life—a life which, to herself who endured or enjoyed it, possessed as great a dimension as the life of the mightiest to himself. Upon her sensations the whole world depended to Tess—' "

"That's marvelous!" Joey interrupted. "Please mark that, too, Mrs. Marsan. The part beginning 'but a woman living her precious life.' "

While Mrs. Marsan was bracketing the chosen lines, a sharp knock admitted Adrian Larsch.

"Edna here?" She gave one look around and hurried on before anybody had time to answer. "Please give her this note for me. Tell her she can slip the answer under my door." She handed Pearl an envelope.

"Miss Larsch, you're the very one!" Joey blurted. 'What is pachydermatous?"

Mrs. Marsan was pleased to see how Adrian's smooth forehead shirred with perplexity. She's stuck. There's a lot she don't know, I bet. If only Mr. Ingalls was here now, and *he* knew. Wouldn't be surprised if he knew more than her, the stacks of library books he's always lugging to and from. . . .

"In what sense is it used?" Adrian forgot her rush.

Mrs. Marsan read the whole passage again.

"But of course!" Adrian breathed relief. "*Pach* as in packhorse, not *patch* as in patchquilt! It's from the Greek *pachys,* thick, and *derma,* skin."

"No wonder, Pearl," Joey said guiltily. "We were looking for patch as in patchquilt."

"Well, what does it mean?" Mrs. Marsan challenged.

"*Thick-skinned.*" Adrian stung her with a look.

"If who wrote that story mean thick-skinned, then why don't he *say* thick-skinned," Pearl objected.

Adrian was staring at the dust jacket, the shadow of alarm in her eyes.

"Is that *Shaw?*"

"It's *Tess,*" Joey said. "*Tess of the D'Urbervilles.*"

"Oh. Thomas Hardy. Corn of yesterday's planting." Adrian drew a deep breath and smiled. "I *thought* I knew my Shaw better than that—though the title on the jacket is his." She added quickly: "Isn't it?"

"I guess so." Mrs. Marsan looked. "I've got more use for the cover than for the book."

"I'm more familiar with his plays. *Pygmalion. Candida. Arms and the Man.*"

"That the kind of play *I* want to be familiar with," Pearl grumbled. "Arms and the Man."

Adrian studied Pearl.

"I have something to say to you, Pearl," she announced.

Pearl went to the door with Adrian. Mrs. Marsan continued without hearing a syllable of what she read. Her ears were in the hall. Pearl and Adrian were having words. She could catch only a few frozen scraps from Adrian, but Pearl was louder and more lavish. "My tongue mine and nobody going to tell me how to use it, thank you ma'am!" Mrs. Marsan heard Adrian insist with quiet emphasis: ". . . can at least be *sure* before you speak . . ." "I speak when I feel like! *Nobody* sure of everything they say. If they got to take time making sure they got no time left to say it!" ". . . criminally erroneous report concerning Mr."—the name was lost in Adrian's lowered voice—"and Jean Lan—" Pearl interrupted: "I got a right to be wrong sometimes!" and a minute afterward she screamed: "How *could* I get them mixed up with them when I don't know it till now you tell me?"

Pearl returned to the living room furious.

"She got a nerve, lecturing *me!* Good if somebody give *her* a sermon on being so stuck-up and God-almighty!" She took the envelope out of her pocket and looked at it angrily. "Son-of-a-butcher," she said under her breath.

"Come sit down and listen to the story, Pearl," Joey ordered.

Mrs. Marsan was contemplating the letter in Pearl's hand.

"What's Larsch writing Edna about, I wonder?"

Pearl turned the envelope over.

"She forgot to glue it," she said. "Lessee."

"Pearl!" Joey put out her hand. "Don't do that! She didn't forget. That's the polite way!"

"If it was anything really private she wouldn't have been polite," Mrs. Marsan said.

"Miss Edna going to tell you, anyhow." Pearl shrugged. "You might's well know now."

Adrian was interested in the ship sailing for South America in April. She intended to take a sabbatical leave from school. If there was any difficulty about booking, she was sure she could overcome it by producing proof that the trip was an educational necessity in connection with her profession.

2

The scrapbook was more than half full. In a couple of months it would be succeeded by a second volume. The pages were heavily patterned with clippings of the Daily Watchword, charm tips, and odd bits of newspaper interest pasted in promiscuously without any attempt at orderly mating. Only the first page showed an indication of design. It was bare except for a square inch of newsprint glued precisely in the middle, like a jewel in a setting. This was Mrs. Marsan's favorite Watchword and she liked to keep it where she could turn to it readily.

She puzzled over whether the Watchword in this morning's paper was worth cutting out. It was neither cheerful nor particularly inspiring, being an old saying to the effect that life is an onion and one peels it crying. She sat at the bridge table in Mr. Cernak's chair, her scissors in one hand and her coffee cup in the other, sipping and thinking. She did not feel like that about life. Granted it was an onion, what had more flavor? And for every tear shed in the peeling, was there not a smack of the lips in the tasting? She decided the scrapbook would be better off without the onion outlook on life.

Alongside the Daily Watchword was the Daily Horoscope, which Mrs. Marsan had read the first thing this morning. Now she read it again, and observed with satisfaction how closely it hit to the happenings of the day. "Since the sun is in Capricorn, no chances should be taken at this time with matters involving money." She had turned an asbestos ear to Sig's hot hunches, and the latest reports from Gulfstream Park proved her two dollars richer for her resistance. "Quiet entertainment should distinguish the afternoon hours"—reading with Pearl and Joey. "A visitor and a message"—Adrian Larsch and her note. "Be on the lookout for unexpected situations which might prove serious." That must have been Edna's having found the lichees and coming home sooner than they thought. It might have been serious if Edna had not judged the book by its cover.

Mrs. Marsan interrupted her check to consider Lady, pawing at her knee. Lady's black eyes showed bright and intense through her shaggy bangs. Her tongue hung out of the side of her mouth like a pennant. Mrs. Marsan reached for a chocolate cream, the last of Jessamine's gift box, and offered it to her. Lady inhaled it diffidently and walked away. It was the first time she had ever been known to refuse anything to eat. Mrs. Marsan was disturbed about her. She made a mental note of stepping down to Doc Kincaid's and getting her a dose of buckthorn.

Returning to the stars, Mrs. Marsan found that the evening hours were ideally suited to letter writing. There was likewise a decided tendency toward romance in the air. Heavy type at the end reminded her that for ten cents and a self-addressed, stamped envelope she could get her horoscope for the first three months of the current year.

Mrs. Marsan found pen and paper and ordered her horoscope, printing her name and the date of her birth. Tomorrow was Sunday; her letter would not be delivered until Monday, and she wanted a speedy reply. She decided to get a special-delivery stamp for the self-addressed envelope when she went down for the buckthorn.

Letter writing. . . . That fulfilled everything. Except the romance. . . .

Lady was acting strangely. She had gotten up from the floor and jumped on the sofa. Now she was back again, languishing on her side at Mrs. Marsan's foot. Restlessness and loss of appetite. Now, if you were a human being, Lady, I would say the trouble with you was—

Love. With a jolt Mrs. Marsan realized. She remembered with new meaning the scenes behind the tavern these last two mornings when she passed by with Lady on leash. Nick Dinapolis' Dalmatian was kenneled in the parking area back of the kitchen, where a wire fence enclosed a neat doghouse and short run. This morning the racket had brought Nick out to see what the trouble was.

What Lady needed was not buckthorn, but a bridegroom. Either was to be had at the drugstore, along with the special-delivery stamp.

"Lord Dundee is an aristocrat, Lady." Mrs. Marsan reached down at the cost of her breath and stroked Lady's head.

Romance in the air. . . . It was wonderful how completely the Daily Horoscope worked out. . . .

3

At ten-thirty Mrs. Marsan started down with her letter and Lady. The idea of surrendering Lady to royalty brought back to her mind a phrase which had never actually been absent from it for several days. *In His Majesty's Service.* She turned around abruptly.

Jean came to the door in Vivien's jade flannel robe and instinctively Mrs. Marsan looked at the pocket.

"I was wondering," she said, "if you had any letters to mail. I'm going down to mail this, and I just thought—"

"No, I haven't any." Jean stood in the doorway, frail as fern. "Thank you just the same."

There was a pause in which Mrs. Marsan did not attempt to go.

"I thought maybe you'd answered that letter?" she hinted.

Jean shook her head. "No," she said simply.

"But you're going to, aren't you?" A letter with crowns on it— "Aren't you?"

"It wasn't for me."

Mrs. Marsan sickened with disappointment.

"It had your name on it, didn't it?" she asked weakly.

"Yes, but there must be some mistake. I think I ought to give it back to the postman."

"Oh." Relief. "Then you didn't yet?"

Somehow Mrs. Marsan and Lady were inside.

"I'm going to." Jean went over to the Coney Island clock and took the letter from the side of one of the two supporting cupids. "It's thanking me for a dress. I didn't send anybody any dress."

Mrs. Marsan sank into the renovated chair, her hand over her heart.

"But you did! Don't you remember—" she gulped, her eyes wide "—that afternoon, sewing at Joey's—"

"I sewed, but I didn't *send* anything."

"You sent your sewing, didn't you? The church gave the names of all the people who did the sewing," she invented glibly, "along with the clothes."

Jean looked at the letter she held. "I still don't feel I did anything to be thanked for."

"Then you can do something to be thanked for right now. Sit down and write that poor woman an answer. It will warm her up on the inside. She's probably freezing on the outside."

"It's from a man," Jean said.

"A *man!* Are you *sure?*"

"He says Madame Blanche Joubert can't write English so she asked him to write for her."

"Dear, you go over to my place and get the pen and ink and paper. I left them on the table. The latch is off. Just walk right in."

"I don't know what to say," Jean protested.

"I'll tell you what to say."

Jean put the letter on the table. When she was gone, Mrs. Marsan drew it from its envelope and scanned it avidly. Belgium. She couldn't pronounce the name of the town. "My dear Miss Landry—" The handwriting was not large, but strong and clear and masculine. Madame Blanche Joubert was delighted with the dress. Since she spoke and wrote only French and Flemish. . . . He was a Canadian soldier, presently serving with the British Army of Rehabilitation. He hoped Miss Landry would pardon the liberty, occasioned by the unusual circumstances. . . . Mrs. Marsan had never read a more polite or proper letter. Hearing Jean's returning steps, she hastily turned to the end for the signature. Eric Arnold.

When Jean came in the letter was back in its envelope on the table. Mrs. Marsan again comfortably overflowed the tapestried chair, Lady at her feet.

Jean sat down and resigned herself to the ordeal. She wrote the date and "Dear Mr. Arnold" and waited for Mrs. Marsan to begin.

"You tell him it was a real pleasure to hear Madam Blanche got the dress." Mrs. Marsan waited. "Have you got that?"

"All right," Jean said.

"Tell him you hope it's not too bad in Europe this winter. Tell him you wish you could send him and Madam Blanche a nice parcel of the lovely springlike weather we've been having in New York for the last few days, but you don't know how long it will last—"

Mrs. Marsan's observations on the weather ran into considerable wordage. She could see the page filling up from where she sat.

"I guess that's about enough now." She thought. "Now for a nice ending. Tell him to tell Madam Blanche to keep her courage up and just to remember—" she recalled a line of Watchword philosophy from the scrapbook "—just to remember the stars are shining even when you can't see them." She waited for Jean to get it down. "Tell him you hope he'll write again for Madam Blanche because you'll always be glad to have news of her, and you wish her lots of luck and to him too."

Jean finished: "Wishing you both lots of luck, Sincerely," and hesitated.

"Jean Landry," Mrs. Marsan dictated.

The envelope was addressed and the letter sealed. Mrs. Marsan said she would stamp it and Jean insisted on paying for the stamp.

"I made you write it. I ought to pay for sending it."

"It costs five cents to mail a letter to Europe," Jean said.

She went to her bedroom and came out with a nickel.

"You can't have many of them left," Mrs. Marsan remarked.

"I'll manage," Jean said grimly.

"I still have that ad of Macy's, if you're ever interested. I guess the Red Door is always open."

"Thank you for the pen and paper. All I had was a pencil."

"That's all right," Mrs. Marsan said.

The hands of the Coney Island clock met as in prayer and midnight sounded in a tinny little orison. Mrs. Marsan noticed what jolly fat bellies the chalk cupids on either side had.

"The drugstore is closed now. I'll get stamps and mail these in the morning."

She looked at the letters, the one ordering her horoscope, the other for Eric Arnold. They felt heavy. It was like holding Fate in her hands, she thought.

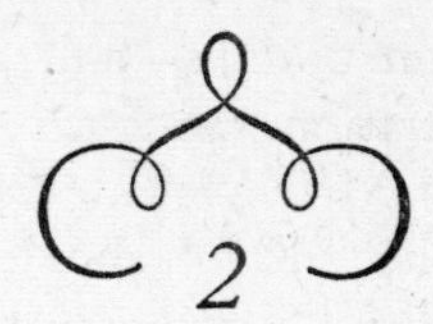

THE FRIENDLY weather continued. Sunday was blue and gold, too pale to be perfect, but a bold counterfeit of spring none the less. The pigeons housed atop the tavern were deceived into vernal cooing, making love noises like the notes of a flute. Family groups and couples, bright in their Sabbath best, walked past quietly to Pastor Frankel's church, only a few blocks away, and for all the shiny cars whizzing up the street and an occasional heavy-breathing bus, there was a kind of happy hush in the air as if nobody wanted to scare the sunshine away.

Mrs. Marsan thought it would be a good idea to give Lady another turn in the open before bringing her in to Lord Dundee. It was a nice day for a wedding, she observed, looking up at the sky—almost Junelike. Lady, freshly washed and combed, was not an unbeautiful bride. Mrs. Marsan had used her own scented soap on her, brushed her with her own nylon bristles until she fluffed out like a ball of kapok.

They made the tour of the gas station, coming back by way of the tavern kitchen as usual. The effect of Lady's grooming was not lost on Nick Dinapolis' Dalmatian. Mildew, Joey Brent called him, on account of his blotched coat. A few of his spots were erased by past attacks of the mange and his shape showed that of the more fattening leftovers from the adjacent kitchen more found their way into him than into the garbage can; but he had a long, gay tail and his ears were eloquent. When he saw Lady coming his ears stood up in admiration and his tail was a whip of joy. As she passed, his appreciation mounted to frenzy, mixed with howls of despair when Mrs. Marsan pulled her away, a dead unwilling weight at the end of the leash. Mildew watched her leave, up on his hind legs against his cage, beating his head against the wire and barking hoarsely. Nick reached a hairy arm out of the kitchen window and doused him with a pot of cold water.

Entering the drugstore, Mrs. Marsan found Doc Kincaid busy opening up cartons of ice-cream cones. Sig's Ruthie came in a moment after her. Doc made them both wait. In the long mirror decorated with signs of banana splits and sundaes they could see him lining up the opened boxes under the soda fountain.

"How's Maxie?" Mrs. Marsan asked.

"He's fine." Ruthie's smile revealed she was waiting for most of her second teeth. "He eats meat now."

"He was long enough getting around to it," commented Doc, still dour because his licorice had failed.

"You expect a big Sunday?" Mrs. Marsan watched Doc open another box.

"Today I'll sell a hundred cones at a pop."

Ruthie's face set like cement. Mrs. Marsan could feel her counting the boxes in the mirror and memorizing the number for Sig.

"Business good?" Mrs. Marsan asked.

"It's not bad." For Doc this was the admission of a boom. "Basketball has put considerable life in my soda and soft-drink line. Those Bats are hard players and heavy drinkers."

"Bats?"

"The neighborhood boys that meet in my cellar. Mr. Cernak's got it fixed up like a gym club. They call themselves the Boys' Association for Tomorrow. B.A.T.—Bats," Doc explained.

Ruthie was listening with ears wide to catch every word. Her eyes were on Doc like gimlets.

"On Wednesday nights the losing side stakes the winning side to candy," Doc went on, fixing things up under the fountain. "They buy the candy here. Keeps me busy keeping up my stock."

"I guess so," Mrs. Marsan sympathized.

"And if the same side loses twice, then the winning side does the staking, to sort of even things up. They have a slogan: Fair Play and Square Sharing. Mr. Cernak thought it up."

"Does the winning side buy the candy here too?" Ruthie inquired sharply.

"Of course," Doc said. " 'If you can get it here, why get it elsewhere?' That's a slogan *I* thought up."

"It sounds good," Mrs. Marsan granted.

"Those five-cent peanut chews are awfully popular," Doc continued. "But today it's ice-cream cones. Mr. Cernak's going to make a speech from two to two-thirty. Private Property versus Public Peace. To induce all the boys to come he's giving away free ice-cream cones. He told me to have at least a hundred on hand." Doc straightened up and smiled. "The boys always hang around till they've spent their Sunday quarters. No, business isn't bad. I'm thinking of buying a country place in Westchester."

Mrs. Marsan found something confusing in the fact that the Bats would help to establish Doc in private property.

"Well, what will it be?" Doc addressed Ruthie.

"A pack of those peppermint tablets for Papa."

"If he'd lay off the bangtails his digestion would be better." He went around the counter and got the tablets. "Horses are bad for the health—as well as the bank account."

Mrs. Marsan remembered her heartburn and wondered if there really were any connection between the digestive tract and the race-track.

"Papa says they're a nickel," Ruthie said and put down five pennies.

"They're five *good* cents." Doc pushed aside a penny with a hole in it.

"That's *your* penny," Ruthie stated firmly. "Papa found it on the paper stand this morning."

Doc put the penny beside the cash register.

"And that's where it will be tomorrow morning," he said.

Ruthie walked out, stiff as a stick.

"She's inherited her dad's sour stomach in her disposition," Doc observed. "Now, what can I do for you."

"First I want some stamps. Two three's and a special-delivery."

Doc produced the stamps from a back drawer of the register. "I only keep these for customers' convenience," he said. "They come in for a stamp and buy something else."

Mrs. Marsan enclosed the special-delivery envelope and sealed her horoscope order. She put it back in her sweater pocket and pulled out Jean's letter to Eric Arnold. It must take a while for a letter to reach Belgium. An idea struck her.

"How much is air mail to Belgium?"

"It's dear," Doc warned. "Thirty cents a half ounce."

"Give me thirty cents in air mails."

Doc rang up the register again. "Some people must have money to throw away."

"Some people object to other people throwing money away if it's not thrown *their* way," Mrs. Marsan said.

Doc shrugged. "Anything else?"

"About Lady." Mrs. Marsan applied the stamps to Jean's letter. "I've brought her in." She squeezed the coin purse in her sweater pocket to be sure she had Lady's dowry. The crisp five-dollar bill crackled reassuringly. "I'll leave her here."

Doc came from behind the counter and surveyed Lady, his thumbs in his trousers belt.

"She sure is fancy," he decided. "But not so frisky."

Lady, lying on the floor with her nose between her paws, looked up at him sullenly through the frizz of her bangs.

"It never was her nature to be frisky," Mrs. Marsan said. "She's too genteel."

"Well, I have nothing to lose." Doc calculated. "That will be a total of five dollars and forty-six cents, for the stamps and the stud."

Mrs. Marsan took out her coin purse and paid. Doc rang up the register. Mrs. Marsan thought with a sentimental wrench of the heart that for Lady it was the ringing of wedding bells.

They went to the back, where in the pocket handkerchief of a yard boxed in with pickets Lord Dundee ran loose. Mrs. Marsan unleashed Lady. The groom ran to meet her, jubilant, trembling, his stubby tail joyous as a rattle. Lady was coy, cool, tantalizing.

"That terrier's grandfather came straight from Perth," Doc said proudly.

They left the pair together in the yard. The nuptial nook, Mrs. Marsan corrected mentally. She looked down at Lady's leash in her hands. Lady had worn it for the last time as a maiden. Her throat knotted and a mist came into her eyes.

2

Jessamine's chair, though regularly empty the first two Sundays in the month, looked so lonesome. Vivien—why not? Mrs. Marsan had never had her in and with Burt out of town, now was the time.

The flare in Vivien's eyes died down when she saw Mrs. Marsan.

"I thought it was Burt back." Every word dripped disappointment. "He forgot to take his keys."

"If you have nothing else to do, maybe you'd like to come over to my place for coffee," Mrs. Marsan invited. "Mr. Cernak and Jean are there."

Vivien was miserable. Mrs. Marsan could smell it on her like a heavy scent.

"Well, I'm not dressed—"

She was in a pink moiré housecoat that lent a false bloom to her face. The glossy waves and flawless black of her hair showed she had spent her Saturday afternoon at the beauty parlor. She was waiting for Burt down to her fingertips, brightly varnished.

"You look grand," Mrs. Marsan admired. She made a memorandum in her head to let down the hem of the brown georgette hostess she was wearing as usual. Vivien's housecoat swept the floor. "Come just as you are."

"I don't feel comfortable in this thing." Vivien shifted her padded shoulders. "Burt likes it, but it's such a weight. I'll just jump into something else."

As they stood there talking Sig passed by with a letter in his hand.

"Another special for Miss Sands," he grumbled. "With her still out of town her mailbox's so stuffed you couldn't slip a hair in it. I'm getting tired of crawling upstairs to slide letters under her door."

"Is Coral Sands out of town?" Vivien was surprised. "Since when?"

"Since a while." Mrs. Marsan could feel something pass between her and Vivien like a vaguely troubled wind.

"Where?"

"Atlantic City. She's got a job in a floorshow there."

"Oh." The wind passed. "That's good," Vivien said. "Will you come in?"

Mrs. Marsan went in. She thought it would do Jean good to

have to talk to Mr. Cernak. Besides, she found Vivien's apartment interesting. The divan and the velvet pillows and lazy chairs and footstools, to say nothing of the satin bedroom and its soft lights. . . .

"I guess I've been letting myself go since Burt's away," Vivien said from the bedroom. "I've been taking off my girdle as soon as I get home at night. It's such a relief."

"I should say so," Mrs. Marsan agreed. "If I had to be laced up all the time I'd go crazy."

Vivien laughed. "A woman is kind of crazy already where there's a man concerned."

Mrs. Marsan waited a while before she asked, "When's Burt coming home?"

"I'm expecting him any minute." The laugh was gone and Vivien gave way to anxiety. "He's days overdue. He was just going for the holidays, you know."

"Haven't you heard from him?"

"Burt hates to write. If I didn't know that I'd be worried." *But I AM worried—terribly. He's never done that before.* The words were there as clearly as if they had been spoken.

"Didn't he wire or telephone?"

"There's a strike on. He can't."

Mrs. Marsan thought back. Burt had ample time to wire or long distance before the strike set in, but in either case Vivien would have known the point of origin.

"I didn't expect to hear from him the first week he was there." It was as if Vivien were answering Mrs. Marsan's doubts. "His people probably took up every minute of his time."

"Well, I'm sure he's all right," Mrs. Marsan said with conviction.

"Oh, yes, I'm sure." Vivien spoke with an energy that proved she wanted to persuade herself. "I was upset a few days after the first when he didn't return and I had no word from him. I even wrote him care of his brother."

"You did?" Mrs. Marsan jumped with interest.

"He hasn't answered, but as I say, Burt would rather take a beating than write a letter. I don't remember his ever having any correspondence even with his family." Indulgently Vivien pieced out an alibi for Burt. "I suppose he was so close to coming home he just figured he'd do the answering when he got here."

"You can't always depend on letters being delivered, either. Sometimes there're—" Mrs. Marsan sought the word "—slip-ups."

"You know," a shoe dropped softly; "it's funny the way I found Burt's brother's address. One night we were joking and Burt said, 'If I ever get mixed up with a subway train or buried under the Empire State, notify my brother Russ. He's got an office in Detroit in the Penobscot Building.' I said all right, I wouldn't have any trouble at all recalling Villars, but Penobscot was a strain on the memory. Burt said, 'Just remember Pen—that's the instrument of notification. Then look in the Detroit phone book and pick out the Villars whose address starts that way.' It all sounded crazy and we laughed over it." Mrs. Marsan heard the bedroom lights click off. "But that's just what I did."

"That's remembering by matching ideas," Mrs. Marsan said. "The way I do it is by pictures. Now me, I would have pictured a pen stuck in the phone book."

Vivien came out in a navy blue wool skirt and loose jacket.

"That's nice." Mrs. Marsan wondered why it was nice when it was so plain. "Sort of soft and easy-looking," she tried to explain it.

"It's a Marie Louise country casual. I did it in brown for an Englishwoman, then copied it in blue for myself. I'd live in it if it weren't for Burt. He likes things on the lush side."

"Different men are different," Mrs. Marsan delivered sagely. "Henry used to like me in a hoover."

As they turned toward Mrs. Marsan's apartment, they heard running up the stairs, heavy, precipitate—a man in a hurry. The sun rose in Vivien's face.

"That must be Burt." She was so glad she trembled.

Doc Kincaid stood on the landing. His graying reddish hair was disarranged and there was mud on his hands and face. His watery eyes found Mrs. Marsan.

"She's gone," he said, his lips tight and colorless.

"Who's gone?" Mrs. Marsan, blanching, leaned against the doorframe for support.

"That damned poodle of yours." Doc Kincaid's lips loosened and anger blazed in his face. "She bit him. She tried to bite me too. I pried her off his leg with a picket. I wanted to bring her back up here but she got away and ran up the street like a fire engine. I've got a mind to sue you and that goddamn dog for damages!" He scowled at the rent in his shirtsleeve.

Mrs. Marsan made a convulsive start as if to rush down into the street and after Lady. She teetered for a moment, her hand on her heart.

Apparently nothing could dent Jean's apathy, but the disturbance brought Mr. Cernak wild-eyed into the hall.

"Come on," he said to Doc. "Show me in which direction she ran. Maybe I can catch her."

The sun had set in Vivien's eyes. "If there's anything I can do—" she offered mechanically.

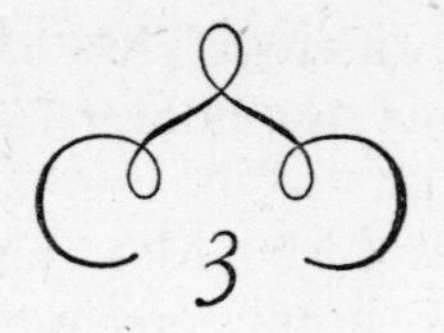

ON WEDNESDAY morning the bell rang long and loudly as if someone were leaning against it. Mrs. Marsan awoke from a short night's sleep to a room still dark. She turned on the light and as she struggled into her kimono glanced over at the clock which she had brought in from the living room and placed on the dresser. It was only ten minutes to six.

Her first thoughts flew to Lady. Somebody was bringing her back. Mr. Cernak's efforts to stop her flight on Sunday afternoon were totally fruitless; he found no trace of her however far and wide he covered the neighborhood. But through Duffy he had called an emergency meeting of the Bats and all the boys had pledged their help in the search. Donegan, the policeman, did what he could. He knew Lady well. He went himself to the Pound, but of the two white poodles picked up since Sunday, neither was Lady. He had been asking all the school children crossing the street if they had seen any sign of her.

In the meantime, Mrs. Marsan ran an ad in the paper offering a reward. By Tuesday afternoon several poodles had been presented only to be immediately identified as strangers. It was not until Tuesday night that a clue to Lady's disappearance developed. Jessamine, on her return from the tavern, reported that Nick's Dalmatian had chewed his way out of his enclosure and was missing since Lady was. It was true that Jessamine's imagination under the influence often ran to fantastic suppositions about animals, but in this case Mr. Cernak had gone at once to the tavern and confirmed the fact.

Of course, it might be merely another spurious attempt to replace Lady and collect the reward. But as Mrs. Marsan buzzed for the caller to come up she hoped fiercely for the best.

It was the special-delivery man with a letter.

"You girls around here sure are popular," he said through a yawn. "Every time I see a special stamp now I turn straight this way from habit."

Mrs. Marsan took the letter from him and recognized her own handwriting in the address. It was her horoscope. Ordinarily she would have crackled with excitement, but in the black silence of early morning she felt more concerned about Lady's present than her own future. She knew the weather had changed during the night; the windowpanes were frosty in the corners when she went to bed after three. And Lady out without her sweater. . . . She shivered, for Sig had not yet sent the heat on.

"Pretty mean outside?" she asked.

"You said it." The man blew on his hands. "You can't expect spring to stay long in January."

"I'd give you a cup of coffee," Mrs. Marsan apologized, "but it's not made yet."

"I got a couple more deliveries to do. I wonder would it be made by the time I got back?" The man had a cavernous smile.

"There's only one thing I do faster than I make coffee," Mrs. Marsan said. "Drink it."

"Put the water on." He started down the stairs. "I'll be back ten minutes from the time she begins to boil."

The flame of the gas stove felt good. Mrs. Marsan warmed her fingers over it. She shook out the folding table and covered it with a luncheon cloth, the one with the Donald Duck border. Milk pitcher, sugar bowl, spoons and knives. She put the butter out so that it would soften and be easier to spread. There was a whole slab of *streusel* bought from Brinkmann just the evening before.

She was glad somebody was coming for coffee. She would make a gallon of it in the big agate, good and strong. She set out the jumbo cups, and plates for the *streusel.* The water was breaking now in hot hissing bubbles.

She missed Lady with a pain like a nagging tooth. The things she was accustomed to do for years came to her automatically only to be turned away as no longer needful. For two days she had forgotten and almost fixed the morning soup-plateful of coffee-and-milk-soaked bread, sprinkled with sugar. When it was time to walk Lady she looked around with an uneasy urge to be up and out and then remembered. Eating candy while she read was always her weakness. Yesterday, absorbed in her paper, she had tossed a couple of marshmallows from sheer routine; when she got up she found them side by side on the floor, reminding her cruelly. She could not bear to look at Lady's leash, or her sweater. She had hung them away in the kitchen closet. The pastry she had saved for her from Sunday afternoon's interrupted coffee hour was covered over and shoved out of sight in the refrigerator. And last night, sitting late by her window, she did not have to wonder long why her lap was cold. She shifted Mr. Cernak's opera glasses restlessly from the tavern to the gas station to the sidewalk and up the street. Once she mistook a piece of flying paper for running white fur.

Even now she thought she heard the familiar tick of Lady's toenails on the kitchen linoleum and she turned around with a jerk. But it was only the drip of coffee in the pot.

For one hideous moment she thought, suppose Lady never comes back, and sudden loneliness caught and held her. She stood transfixed, listening to the lifeless silence of her rooms as if she could hear it, staring as if she could see it. Mr. Cernak blamed money. But the root of all evil was not the love of money, it was the fear of loneliness. Why did people want money if not to keep from being lonely?

She was glad somebody was coming for coffee. She wished he would hurry.

"When you get your first whiff of heaven it'll smell like java on a cold morning," he said.

He looked older with his cap off because his hair was salted with gray. About forty-five, Mrs. Marsan judged. As he peeled down the zipper of his windbreaker a green-and-black plaid shirt shouted its presence.

Mrs. Marsan had been too busy to dress. She was still in her flannelette pajamas and kimono. Her feet were bare in her felt slippers, and while her permanent was up in its usual style, it showed it had been slept in. Her eyes, her color, everything about her said she had just gotten up from a night of scant sleep. She regretted it dimly, but dismissed her chagrin with a shrug and unhinged a *streusel* for herself from the square.

"Have some butter, Mr.—"

"Bill's the name. Just call me Bill." He helped himself to the butter.

Mrs. Marsan felt better after her first cup.

"It's my horoscope in here." She tapped the letter beside her plate. "I haven't had a chance to read it yet. If you don't mind I'll just take a look at it."

"Go ahead," Bill said. He dipped his *streusel* into the cup, and bent over to bite off the weeping end.

Mrs. Marsan tore open the envelope and pulled out a long sheet of paper typewritten on both sides. Her hands shook in anticipation.

"My wife went to a fortuneteller once," Bill recalled bitterly. "It cost her a dollar and it cost me twenty. The fortuneteller told her how much I won at a poker party the night before."

The page was divided under various headings in italicized type. *General. Health. Finances. Business. Communications. Travel. Affairs of the Heart.* With difficulty Mrs. Marsan restrained herself from trying the impossibility of reading it all at once.

"Look what gives on money," Bill said. "That's what I'd dig for first."

"Let's see. I guess that would be under Finances." Mrs. Marsan found the paragraph. "It says, 'You have keen urges to speculate, but since the opening months of the year are not the best time for risking money, you may suffer several losses.' " She shook her head. "That's the horses," she sighed.

"Cripes, you can lose it fifty times faster on stud poker than on slow ponies!" Bill claimed with pride.

" 'Some increase in income is due in a few weeks,' " Mrs. Marsan read on, " 'but will not stay with you long. A sizeable sum of money will eventually come to you from a long familiar yet unexpected source.' Now what do you think of that!"

"I don't believe in crystal gazing," Bill said doggedly. "It's the bunk. I don't believe in it ever since that fortuneteller told my wife what I won at that poker party."

"Let me pour you another cup of coffee." Mrs. Marsan had to lift the pot with both hands. "Maybe you're like me. I never see things right until after my second."

Bill said, "Don't mind if I do."

"Just listen to this!" She jumped. "Under Communications. 'Exciting activity characterizes the coming months, centering about letters, both domestic and from abroad. Before long you will be called on to communicate with a dark man in another city.' For heaven's sake, who can it be? . . ."

"Letters and love. Women rather get the one or the other than eat," Bill observed scornfully.

"Let's see what it says about love right now." Her eyes dove into Affairs of the Heart. " 'Look for an active part in an early wedding. Also, during the coming months, you may frequently find yourself in hot water. But your dabbling in romance will have favorable consequences even if attending circumstances sometimes becloud the issues.' " She frowned. "It's sort of hard to understand. . . ."

"No, it ain't. It don't say you're going to be in love. It says you're going to be in hot water. Look at it again."

"Well, it means the same thing. 'Hot water' is kind of poetic."

"It's just as poetic in the bathtub." Bill threw his head back and drained his cup.

"Look here under Travel!" She traced the words with a trembling forefinger. " '*March is a month of many changes. The stars say you are destined to go on a very long journey.*' If that's not exciting!"

Bill scratched his head. "I don't care much for that. The idea of a long trip where they don't mention you got to take along any baggage gives me the creeps."

"That's silly," Mrs. Marsan said. Automatically she poured him a third cup. "If you haven't sense enough to take along baggage without being told—"

Bill grinned enormously. "I guess it's just my old man and the Old Country in me. My old man believed in banshees. He said an hour before he died he heard the banshee wailing. Now every time I hear something wailing I get the willies."

"What in the world is a banshee?"

"It's some kind of Irish spirit sets up a howl to let folks know they're all aboard for heaven," Bill explained.

"Oh. Then you're Irish." Banshee. Funny word. . . .

"You find all flavors in New York, lady."

Bill finished his coffee and got up. "I guess I got to go. The life I lead is no better'n a carrier pigeon's." He stretched.

The kitchen skylight had faded from purple to pearl gray. The light was still necessary but it had a jaundiced instead of a jolly glow.

As Bill stepped into the hall, zipping up his windbreaker, Adrian Larsch, off to school, turned from her door directly opposite. It took them a moment to measure each other. Her eyes dropped him to seize Mrs. Marsan's kimonoed figure in the doorway. They were as hard as marbles.

Bill waved a salute. "So long, Toots. Thanks for a swell time."

"Good-by, Bill," Mrs. Marsan said.

Adrian hurried off, without having said good morning. Bill's heavy boots drowned her out on the stairs.

Nice boy. . . .

2

Coral Sands came by just before noon to pick up her laundry. Her leopard skin coat had the drooping air of fatigue to which its uncertain career and several seasons entitled it, and the crazy little coachman's hat she wore looked as if it were too tired to hold on to its precarious perch over one eye and was ready to tumble off at any moment. Coral herself looked worn and weary. Her bright hair was tarnished from having missed its weekly wash and her green eyes were circled. Altogether she had the rumpled appearance of a dress retrieved from the dirty clothes basket and put on without pressing.

Mrs. Marsan handed her the bundle of laundry and twenty-five cents.

"It was four seventy-five," she said.

Coral held out the quarter. "Two-bits to buy Lady a bone."

"Lady's gone. Besides, you better buy yourself a bone. You're getting too thin."

"Well," Coral opened her bag and dropped the quarter into the coin purse, "this will tip Elvie for a shamp and set. My hair hasn't seen water for so long it's turning camel color." She sighed. "I guess it will be Elvira's last tip. After this I've got to economize. I'm joining the ranks of the poor but respectable, Marsie."

Mrs. Marsan eyed her with interest. "When did you get in?" She thought, somebody's going to be mighty glad you're back—Vivien Villars.

"Just now." It was evident that Coral was economizing also on words.

"Have a good time?"

"Grand." A reminiscent flare shot up in her eyes like fireworks.

"Well, you don't mind working hard if you're enjoying your job."

Coral said nothing, but the veiled sideways glance and sullen set of her mouth spoke for her. Busy old bitch. . . .

"With what you earned on this three weeks stand you ought to be living on Easy Street for a while instead of talking about economizing."

"Listen, Marsie." Coral pinned her down with a look. "My bank account is as personal as my bathroom. And it deserves the same privacy." She paused. "Now stop working out crossword puzzles and be yourself, will you?"

"Well," Mrs. Marsan shrugged, "there's no fool like an old fool—unless it's a young one."

Coral looked around for something. "Say—no fancywork—is it true—Lady doesn't live here any more?"

The bleak day showed gray at the window. Back behind the tavern and beside Mildew's empty pen white scabs of ice lay over the ground. Loneliness confronted Mrs. Marsan again. It wouldn't be so bad as long as she kept Coral around.

"Stay for lunch," she invited quickly, "and I'll tell you about it. I've been too bothered to go to the butcher this morning, but we can have fried eggs and some of Brinkmann's *wiener schnitzel*. And hot coffee, of course."

Coral put her bundle down and threw her hat and bag on the sofa. "That's elegant," she said hungrily. "I've got such an appetite I could eat sticks if they were properly seasoned." She slipped off her coat and followed Mrs. Marsan to the kitchen.

Coral listened quietly to the story as she spread the Donald Duck cloth again and set the table with the jumbo plates and cups.

"So Doc wants full value on his shirt. It's prewar, but he says that's *why* it's worth as much and more than a new one, because he couldn't replace it with the same quality now at twice the price. That's five dollars right there." Mrs. Marsan slipped another fried egg off the lifter onto the platter. "Then there's the picket he says Lady busted off when she backed into it. Fifty cents."

"It's nice of him to knock the luxury tax off of those items." Coral had no use for Doc because he refused to give her credit on her cosmetics account.

"I'll have to pay Dundee's hospital bill. It's five dollars a day and he'll be there a week. His leg wasn't just bit into. It was sort of chewed up. Thirty-five dollars minimum, maybe more."

"He didn't say anything about deducting Dundee's feed bill for what he'd eat at home during that time, did he? I suppose he was so excited he overlooked that."

"He did say he'd make a compromise settlement on the stud fee, splitting it to two and a half, and standing the other two-fifty himself, being as the actual contract never came off."

Mrs. Marsan slipped the sixth egg onto the platter and sighed. "The only thing that came off was Lord Dundee's leg—almost."

"That's sweet of him," Coral drawled. "I hope he survives the strain of being noble. He's not used to it."

"Shirt, picket and hospital comes to forty dollars and fifty cents. Less two-fifty refund, thirty-eight dollars. Then there's the ambulance fee, three dollars each way. Thirty-eight and six makes forty-four. Don't it?"

"You'd better figure closer to fifty," Coral advised. "There are always incidentals, you know. And Doc's too goodhearted to leave anything out."

"The trouble is, he wants settlement right away. It's only the middle of the month and if I give him what I have I'll be strapped till the first. I'll have to run down to Sobel with Mr. Cernak's opera glasses, I guess."

Coral started impulsively, "If I had—" Then she remembered she was presently supposed to be rich. She reddened abruptly.

"Sit down," Mrs. Marsan said. "We'll just keep the coffee-pot on the stove where we can reach it."

The kitchen was warm and fragrant with mingled food odors. Coral ate ravenously. "I had such an early breakfast," she explained, helping herself again to the *schnitzel.* Mrs. Marsan wondered if they had had breakfast at all, beyond, perhaps, a snack at some station counter. She kept Coral's cup filled, while working away at her crossword puzzle. The blocks filled in, piecing out the answers. *We stayed till the last cent. All we had left was our return ticket and a few subway fares. . . .* She slid a third egg onto Coral's unprotesting plate.

"Think Elvira can squeeze me in this afternoon?"

"Maybe if you tell her you have a date. Elvira's sentimental."

"I have a date with a job," Coral laughed. "That ought to touch her sentiments. I owe her for a couple of months."

"Those jobs sure believe in sending specials. Sig got a lot of exercise bringing them up."

"Oh, them." Coral crinkled her nose disdainfully. "All from the same jerk. He's got money, but that's all he's got."

"One good thing about them being all from the same party, you have only one answer to make."

"From now on, I'll *always* have only one answer to make," Coral said determinedly. "And the answer is *No*."

Mrs. Marsan remembered the pastry put away for Lady in the refrigerator. She got up and brought it out.

"Here's a dab of dessert. It's left from Sunday, but maybe you won't mind."

"This about the job is straight, Marsie." Coral forked into the pastry with pleasure. "It's an ad I read over a guy's shoulder in the subway. I wrote down the address. A club in the Village. Hatcheck girl. Small salary but tall tips."

"What about your modeling course?"

"That's the beauty of it. I can study by day and slave by night. The course is paid for. All I have to work for is self-support. And while I don't propose to support myself in the style to which I'd like to be accustomed—"

The bell screamed behind Coral, cutting her short.

"Press the buzzer for 'em to come up and go to the door," Mrs. Marsan said quickly. "I'll just run and get into something." She was still in her kimono.

Coral came to the bedroom and said it was Doc Kincaid—he had an additional item of ten cents, covering the arnica he used on Lord Dundee's leg before the ambulance came, that he wanted to tack on to the original account.

"Oh, him." Mrs. Marsan threw her dress back over the chair. "I'm not dressing up for *him*."

She swept into the living room, indignation struggling to undo her dignity. At the sight of Nick Dinapolis she stood suddenly still. He came all the way in, without waiting to be asked. Under his arm he carried what appeared at first glance to be a bundle of gray wadding. It was Lady.

"Ain't this your dog?" he said.

He put her down on the floor. Never before had Lady been so little worthy of the name. She looked like an old goat, matted and dirty. Her bleary eyes were half closed behind her bangs, which were clotted into knotty kinks. She stood there quivering, a wreck of her Sunday self, her rag of a tail tucked between her muddy legs.

With a stunned cry Mrs. Marsan recognized her under the dilapidation.

"Lady!"

She stooped and picked her up, pressing her close, patting her all over.

"I fooled you that time!" Coral fell back on the sofa, laughing uncontrollably. "You thought it was Doc—"

Tears rivered down Mrs. Marsan's face. Nick looked from her to Coral, laughing in fresh fits, as if he were trying to make some sense out of the bewildering emotions of women.

"My God, where did you find her!" Mrs. Marsan's voice shook.

"In the dog pen," Nick said. "Both of them together. They gonna come back when they get good and hungry, you betcha bottom dollar!"

"Where in the world have they *been?*"

"What should *I* know?" Nick was a huge, dark man. When he hunched up his shoulders to a ledge below his ears he looked mountainous. "They been on a honeymoon. It don't make no difference where. Seashore's the same as the woods for that."

Coral grew suddenly serious.

"When she could have had Lord Dundee!" Mrs. Marsan regretted. "I don't understand it."

"Females're funny like that." Nick's thick black eyebrows scowled together into one. "I see it all the time in my business. They leave 'em all to break their necks and pick up with the one they got no right to. They don't use no reason." Nick pronounced *th* like *d*. "Not that I'm making out a case for my dog against yourn," he added gallantly. "That hound of mine's just as hard to savvy. There's a dog with as good a home as ever a dog had. All he can eat, good place to sleep, lotsa affection. And what does he do? Chews hisself out of it to run off somewheres with a ball of fluff—begging pardon—and stays away till they both starve if they stay away any longer. It just ain't reasonable."

"Well, that's love, I guess." Mrs. Marsan looked at Lady fondly.

"Sure it is," Nick agreed. "But it's lousy. That's why I wanta close up the place and go to Florida. Raising oranges ain't so hard to understand."

Nick refused the reward. It was all in the family now, he said. Forget it. . . .

"She must be starving." Mrs. Marsan flew to the kitchen as soon as Nick had gone. "I'll fry her a couple of eggs and I believe there's some *schnitzel* left."

Coral remained sitting on the sofa, thinking.

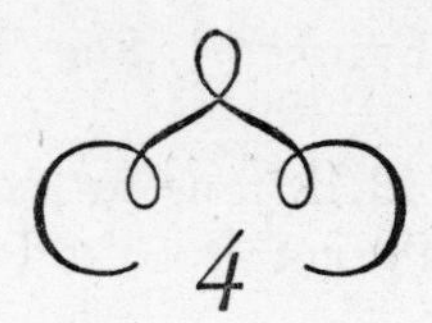

AFTER the receipt of her monthly check, Mrs. Marsan never expected any mail beyond an occasional bill or some sample or recipe she sent for herself. Contrary to custom, the last week in January saw her morning and afternoon waiting impatiently for the postman. As soon as he came she hurried downstairs to the double row of boxes in the vestibule and looked to see if there was yet anything in Jean Landry's.

This afternoon it was there. Through the square glass eye of the box it stared back at her like a buff-colored iris. By squinting she could make out the strip of crowns along one edge.

It was Jean's day to go to the doctor. She had left shortly after two o'clock and might not be back before five—six, if she stopped at any of the stores. It was the worst weather in weeks to be out in; the sleet came down in needles, pricking the puddles in the street to an eyelet pattern, and the wind drove great bias currents cracking against the windowpanes. Mrs. Marsan wondered if the umbrella she lent Jean would stand the strain, or if it would blast upward into a wine glass as it sometimes did.

From three to six was a long time to wait. Why not go over to Joey Brent's for a while and forget that letter?

She remembered too late it was the minister's afternoon. Yet on entering she found he had not arrived.

"Where's Pastor Frankel?" She knew he was always punctual.

"He's not coming." Bells rang in Joey's voice. "He phoned Elvira to say he can't get over today on account of the weather."

"Mean old weather good for something after all," Pearl said.

Mrs. Marsan sank into a chair with relief, and Lady settled into a ball at her feet, prepared to sleep. Lady, restored with soap and water, was her old self except that she slept almost continuously.

"Now that I'm here you can go over to Mrs. Villars, Pearl. Lady and I'll stay with Joey."

"She don't want me this week," Pearl sulked. "She sick in bed and like to be quiet."

"She paid you just the same," Joey reminded.

"Yeh. But I don't get my chance to play around with all that pretty satin and stuff."

"I thought she was looking a little better lately." Mrs. Marsan remembered her in the country casual, ungirdled and relaxed. "She's not getting the flu, I hope?"

"It's nothing she getting," Pearl clarified. "It's something she *losing*."

Mrs. Marsan looked at Pearl and waited.

"Mr. Burt," Pearl stated.

Mrs. Marsan's eyes widened. "Does she *know?*"

"I told her."

"Pearl! You shouldn't have." Joey, at the window, lowered Mr. Cernak's opera glasses—which had been saved a trip to Sobel because Doc condescended to wait for his money, plus five per cent interest—and turned her eyes on Pearl reproachfully. "That was cruel, Pearl."

"Any man two-timing me," Pearl sniffed, "I want to know it. I did her a favor."

"What did she say?" Mrs. Marsan asked breathlessly.

"She didn't *say* anything. She just *asked*."

"Well—*what?*" Pearl was tantalizing.

"First she asked how did I know, so I said Miss Larsch tell me. Right out there—" Pearl thumbed toward the hall "—that day she come to give Miss Edna that note and end giving me a lecture. I was hoping Miss Vivien give her hell."

"Did she?" *Good if she did. . . .*

"Nobody catch Larsch long enough to give her the time of day. But Miss Vivien, she phone her at school. Miss Vivien say, 'Miss Larsch such a lovely person.' I say, 'You must of got the wrong number.' "

"What did they say, Pearl," Mrs. Marsan insisted.

"It was all friendly and polite. When Miss Vivien ask *her* how did she know, she say, *you* told her."

"Me!" *That day on the sidewalk—clearing Mr. Ingalls—to get Adrian to come to the party.*

"She say for Miss Vivien not to pay no attention to it. She say she got good reason to believe—" Pearl broke off, casting sheepishly around the room as if looking for a hole to escape.

"Believe what?"

"I dunno. It was something about people what live in glass houses see only reflections of theirselves."

Mrs. Marsan pondered.

"She's got that wrong. She's not so smart. She's always getting her quotations mixed up. It should be, 'gather no moss.' "

"Anyhow, now Miss Vivien don't believe it—I mean, about Mr. Burt. She say to me today, 'Pearl, that all a horrible mistake. Never mention it again.' I say to myself, Mister Cupid sure got cataracts on both his eye! But I feel so sorry for her I keep my mouth shut."

"I suppose she really don't believe it," Mrs. Marsan said. "When a woman loves a man like that, it's funny how she can hypnotize herself into believing anything."

"You ask *me,* she got sickened up trying to make herself believe she really *do* believe she don't believe it."

"Did she say anything to him?"

"She not going to. She say she wouldn't hurt his feelings." Pearl drew herself together in the attitude of a crouching animal. A hard glint grew in her narrowed eyes. "Me, *I'd* hurt his feelings. Time I'd finish with him he wouldn't have no feelings."

"Pearl, I heard you say yourself once nobody could ever be sure about anything," Mrs. Marsan recalled.

"Maybe not sure, but so darn suspicious it's practically the same thing. Don't I notice they go off the same day? Don't I know they come back the same day?" Pearl burst into a ribald laugh. "If they not got perfect timing!"

"Oh, shut up, Pearl," Joey said disgustedly. She had not uttered a word until now, never taking the glasses from her eyes. "Can't you think of anything but men? Come here and see something."

Mrs. Marsan and Pearl went to the window.

"Look. I bet that's an ex-serviceman down there waiting for the bus. He's been waiting nearly twenty minutes. He must be soaked."

Through the scrim of sleet they saw a man on crutches, a bandaged foot big and shapeless as a club tucked up from the flooded curb. Mrs. Marsan borrowed the glasses. Nice-looking fellow . . . young. . . .

"The way those bus running lately he planted to wait till he sprout." Pearl was always quarreling with the bus schedule.

"Lend him an umbrella, Pearl," Joey ordered. "Go on. The big black one."

"I can't lend him a hand to hold it with," Pearl said stubbornly.

"Ask him in," Mrs. Marsan suggested. "That's the thing to do. He's probably frozen."

"Go get him, Pearl," Joey said.

"Me? In that ice soup?"

"Put on Edna's old boots. They're in the kitchen closet. And throw the oilcloth off the table over you."

A minute later Pearl went out in seven-leaguers and a poncho imprinted with fruits and flowers. "Can't *think* of men," she mumbled, "but got to go out chasing them."

From the window Mrs. Marsan and Joey watched the invitation being extended and accepted, the opera glasses changing hands every ten excited seconds.

2

Pearl served the hot chocolate and macaroons intended for the minister.

"I used to dream about things like this when I was out on Okinawa," Phil Cassidy said. "Chocolate—cake—ice cream. We called them the Big Three."

He stood propped on his crutches with his back to the radiator, soaking up the heat. Now, with his hat and overcoat off, he looked about twenty-five. A ragged gash scarred the left side of his face, but the humor in his brown eyes and a quick, easy way he had of smiling defeated its effect. His hair was crisp and brush thick, not much darker than his sunburned skin.

"It's funny the things people will dream about," Mrs. Marsan observed. "I hate to dream I'm falling. I fall *up*, and it's such a foolish feeling."

"I love to dream anything," Joey said warmly. "It's so adventurous!"

"Well, don't dream of the past," Phil smiled. "That's a sign of old age."

He finished his chocolate and set the cup and saucer on the table.

Lady stirred, roused at length by the smell of food. Absent-mindedly Mrs. Marsan broke off a piece of macaroon and tossed it to her. She snapped it sleepily out of the air. Aware of a new presence, she got up, stretched and went over to Phil. He reached down to pat her, his broad shoulders lying loosely on their props. Lady braced against his knees, offering her ears for scratching.

"Nice little pooch. What's her name?" He raised his eyes to Joey.

"Lady Hamilton. Mrs. Marsan called her just Lady, but I put the Hamilton to it. Lady Hamilton was so exciting! I read a novel about her once." Once. Joey wondered whatever Edna did with the book.

"She'll have to do some romancing to live up to *that* name."

"She started Sunday," Mrs. Marsan put in.

Phil chuckled. "Did she?" and began to stroke her head with his other hand. For the first time Mrs. Marsan noticed he had not removed his left glove. *But it can't be. . . . He even held the saucer in that hand and the fingers curved in a normal enough grip on the crutch. . . .*

Lady withdrew diffidently and sniffed in detail at the outstretched leather palm, nozzling curiously under the cuff. She kept her nose glued there for a moment, drawing in noisy, puzzled breaths. Then, having decided, she wagged her tail giddily and went for the ungloved hand, working her head up into its warmth.

Phil threw his head back and laughed.

"You choosy little devil, you!" He rumpled her ears and bangs together and made a handful of her moist snout. "You certainly have your preferences, haven't you?"

"She certainly has." Mrs. Marsan was thinking of Nick's Mildew.

"I'm crazy about her," Joey said almost violently. "I wish she was mine."

"Isn't she?"

"No, she's mine," Mrs. Marsan glowed. "But if the stork brings any packages, one of them's for Joey."

Phil said "Oh?" and then changed it to "Oh, I see." He stopped the rough play and petted Lady gently.

"Sit down," Joey suggested. "You must be dried out by now."

Phil took a chair and folded his crutches against the arm. Lady curled before the warmth of the radiator and went back to sleep.

"Dogs make good company," Phil remarked. "Nice if you had one. How do you fill in the empty corners of the day?"

"Oh, there's always something to see from the window. Pigeons. People. Washlines. Trees."

"Trees around here?"

"Two of them," Mrs. Marsan informed him.

"Then there are the customers from the beauty shop just below," Joey chatted on. "They look brand-new when they come out simonized."

"You're getting mixed up with the gas station, Joey," Mrs. Marsan said.

"Feeding the birds on the window sill is fun. But I have the most fun when it snows. The kids come out with their sleds. Sometimes they have snowball fights. And it's a big excitement on days when the coal comes. I like to hear it rattle into Sig's cellar. Then there's the garbage pick-up. The overseer is grand. He smokes a cigar and wears a diamond ring on his little finger."

"It takes a good pair of eyes to see any glamour in garbage," Phil said with a curious interest. "Go on. Tell me some more."

"Joey even sees poetry in wet pajamas," Mrs. Marsan marveled. "Whether the wind's high and they dance, or the day's quiet and they droop, to me, they're still wet pajamas."

"Maybe it's just because," Joey touched the glasses in her lap, "everything looks dramatic through a pair of opera glasses."

"I don't know." Phil rubbed his scarred cheek thoughtfully. "Lots of people would look at pajamas through opera glasses and see only the holes and the tears in them."

"You're right," Mrs. Marsan agreed. "I've looked till I'm dizzy and I don't see any resemblance in that sourpuss of a mounted policeman who goes riding past here to that Sir Laughs-a-lot Joey says he reminds her of."

"Sir Laughs-a-lot?"

"*Lancelot,*" Joey corrected. "He's a character in a book of poems my sister gave me. The poem is 'The Lady of Shalott.' "

Phil smiled. " 'And moving thro' a mirror clear that hangs before her all the year, shadows of the world appear.' "

" 'And sometimes thro' the mirror blue the knights come riding two and two: she hath no loyal knight and true—' "

Joey broke off, and they laughed together, a little self-consciously.

"I keep a couple of lines from your Tennyson with me all the time," Phil said.

"What are they?"

" 'That men may rise on stepping-stones of their dead selves to higher things.' "

Though Mrs. Marsan did not quite understand it, she would have liked it for her scrapbook. It sounded nice. . . .

"Listen!" Phil's enthusiasm went off like a firecracker in the silence that had settled. "You can get around, you know. The same as me." He laid his hand on his crutches. "Why don't you try with these?" His expression reversed. "I guess they wouldn't do. I'm too much taller."

"Oh, I have a pair," Joey said. "The finest Edna could buy."

"Well! Why don't you use them?"

"The first day I tried, I fell. And Edna got so frightened she put them away and I never tried again."

"They still where she hid them," Pearl's voice came from the kitchen. "They look at me longing-like every time I take out the ironing board."

"One fall doesn't make a failure," Phil said. "It takes time, patience, practice. Listen." He leaned forward. "I can teach you. I work six days a week for an advertising firm in Manhattan—commercial drawing—but I get every Wednesday afternoon off. I can come Wednesdays and help you."

The light in Joey's face went out. "The minister comes on Wednesdays."

"Just as good if he comes on Thursdays," Mrs. Marsan said promptly.

A sour echo rumbled from the kitchen. "Better he don't come at all."

"I don't know if Edna would want to tell him," Joey worried.

"*I'll* tell him," Mrs. Marsan offered. "And listen. Why do you have to tell Edna about anything. Why don't you just learn to use your crutches in secret and then some day when you know how, walk right out to meet her in the hall and surprise her!"

"Do you think I could?" Joey turned to Phil eagerly.

"Of course you can!"

The sleeting had stopped, leaving the wind to drive through the streets alone. The afternoon grayed prematurely and Pearl came in and turned on the two lamps.

"My sister may be home now," Phil said. "Is there a phone around?"

"Drugstore or candy shop," Mrs. Marsan advised. "The phone trade's just one of the things they fight over."

"I'll give Brenda a ring. You wouldn't know my sister—Brenda Simms? She and her husband live three blocks down. They have two kids—boys."

Mrs. Marsan shook her head.

"You know," Phil got into his overcoat, "funny thing. I didn't think of phoning her from the office this morning. I didn't think of phoning for a taxi back to the subway—that's the way I came. And I could have gone to the tavern, or waited at the gas station for the bus. But I just stood out there playing statues in the sleet. Now what do you think prompted me to do a fool thing like that?"

"The bus was to blame," Joey claimed. "It took so long."

Mrs. Marsan knew better. She knew the whole thing was arranged by the inscrutable Forces of Fate.

3

The Bats were dragging something down to the drugstore cellar. There was an odd familiarity about the weather-worn end of what looked like a large wooden box.

Mrs. Marsan went into the drugstore and with her last thirty cents—she would have to run credit at Brinkmann's—bought an air-mail stamp. She hurried right out because she wanted to drop by Sig's and hear the results of the Hibiscus Stakes, but she found the Gone for Supper sign in his door. Though she had been too short of cash to place a bet, she was curious to know how Sig's favorite for the sixth race fared. She hovered around for a minute, wondering why the store seemed different. Perhaps it was because of the stillness.

When, gripping the rail, she reached the top of the stairs and leaned there recovering her breath, Jean came out in her jade flannel robe carrying the borrowed umbrella.

"I was just coming to return this," she said.

Mrs. Marsan was pleased. She had been spared the necessity of inventing an excuse to call on Jean.

"Come on in a minute."

"I—"

"Just for a minute." Mrs. Marsan had her by the arm. They went in and sat on the sofa.

"What did the doctor say?" Mrs. Marsan prefaced.

"I'm to continue with the capsules. But my hemoglobin is ninety-two and my blood pressure's raised to normal—for the first time."

"That's good." She could wait no longer. "Get any mail today?"

"A letter from Mr. Arnold."

"Well, I declare! Did he have much to say?"

"Madame Blanche sent her love."

"For heaven's sake. Is that all? Didn't *he* send anything?"

"Oh, that's not all," Jean said. "Madame Blanche is moving to another town to live with her married daughter because her own house and everything was destroyed and she's all alone."

"Don't he say anything about *himself?*" She was getting impatient.

"Yes, he says he's afraid he's too sentimental—"

"Uh-um." This was better. "Go on—"

"—because he's so deeply affected when he sees skinny dogs searching for scraps in empty garbage cans."

"Oh, shucks." Mrs. Marsan fell back.

"One day he saw a big starving borzoi, and he knew he ought to shoot it and put it out of its misery, but he just couldn't. And afterward he blamed himself. And he feels terrible when he sees small boys setting traps in the snow for birds—not because the boys are really horrid but because they're hungry."

"Don't he talk about anything but buzzards and birds?" she demanded irritably.

"Yes, I told you. Madame Blanche." Jean gave her a wondering look.

"Well, when all the birds are caught and with Madam Blanche out of the way, he'll have to write about something else," Mrs. Marsan said, satisfied.

"Oh, he won't be writing any more. He was just writing for Madame Blanche."

"*What?*" She sat up. "Won't he answer your letter?"

"But I'm not going to send him any letter. There's no need."

"No *need!*" Mrs. Marsan jumped into the breach of this new situation, desperately fighting for ground. "You wouldn't let that poor man die over there of loneliness, would you? Think of what letters mean to him! He's helping other people, cold and hungry doing it. You can help him, steam-heated and well fed. Now can't you?"

"Well—"

"You answer this very night." Mrs. Marsan breathed more freely. "Wait. I'll get you the pen and ink. You can take them back with you. And some paper."

"He addressed me 'Miss' Landry. So I think I ought to tell him—about—that I'm a widow." Jean's voice stuck. "But I can't—tell him how—"

"You don't have to," Mrs. Marsan said gently. "Just be chatty and cheerful." She returned stubbornly to the main idea. "Didn't he say *anything* personal?"

Jean thought.

"Oh. Somewhere he mentions about being a bachelor."

"Does he?" That was perfect. It would have been a calamity if— Her spirits revived. "I have an air-mail stamp I've been wanting to get rid of for ages. You'd do me a favor to use it!"

Jean apparently thought it not strange that Mrs. Marsan should carry the stamp around in her sweater pocket.

"I suppose I *should* answer by air. *He* did. How much is it?"

"Nothing. Somebody gave it to me."

"Well, thanks a lot."

Jean took the stamp and dropped it in the envelope.

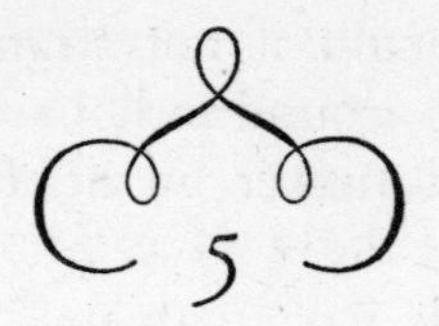

THE TALK with the minister had been smooth and successful. He was delighted to hear Joey was taking sewing lessons on Wednesdays and would be glad to rearrange his schedule to come on Thursdays. He was sorry so many ladies in the neighborhood failed to find time for church occasionally, but he was pleased to know the defection was due, in Mrs. Marsan's case at least, to an invalid—not an indifferent—heart. Indeed, yes—he knew Mrs. Brenda Simms! Member of his congregation. A very fine young wife and mother. Why did Mrs. Marsan ask? Nothing wrong at the Simmses, he hoped? Excellent people. . . . Mrs. Marsan replied, without fibbing, that everything was wonderful at the Simmses, which was the way she felt since her check-up assured that Phil's folks were nice.

Mrs. Marsan came away with the luxurious feeling of having accomplished a double mission. She was wearing her black sailor with the plush violets, and corseted under her coat, with Joey's studded squirrel pinned on the lapel, she felt self-confident if uncomfortable. It was genteel to wear one's best when calling on a man of the cloth. Only on one point was she annoyed with a pricking of guilt: recently she had read it was The Correct Thing to keep the glove on when shaking hands, but to her it seemed cold and unfriendly. She regretted not having removed hers, even though the openwork the moths had left in the gauntlet would have showed.

With money in her purse again since yesterday, she could hold out a couple of dollars' bait to luck. She wondered if Sig had the returns yet.

There was no one in the store and he was at the radio when she walked in. Somehow the back of his head looked sour. The broadcast from Hialeah was just signing off. Sig killed the hurrying voice with an angry click of the dial.

"She would have made it"—he kicked at a chair—"but that rotten rider they give her got her away from the gate in a tangle and she couldn't get clear for the first half mile."

"Dizzy Babe?"

Sig gulped and shook his head. He looked as if he wanted to cry.

"She was the best longshot filly on the card."

"After this you keep your longshots," Mrs. Marsan said. "What I want is a sure shot. How about Queen Vic in the dash for mares?"

"She got shuffled back in the early going and was necked out by Pink Pajamas."

Mrs. Marsan raised her shoulders and let them drop. "And I thought this was my lucky day."

"If you think *you* got troubles—" Sig drew his hand through his oiled, shoestringy hair.

"Maybe if you saw somebody else's you'd be glad to keep yours," Mrs. Marsan advised. "Ever hear of St. Peter's washline? Everybody was complaining. So he hung their troubles out and told them they could all have their pick. And everybody rushed for their own."

"I wouldn't pick anything like what Kennedy handed me yesterday. My lease run out last month and the bank's not going to renew it. Notice anything about this building?"

Mrs. Marsan recalled the idea she had Wednesday evening that there was a difference in Sig's store.

"I had a feeling something was funny—"

"Didn't you hear the hammering a while ago?"

"I've been out."

"Take a look when you leave here. For sale sign."

Mrs. Marsan whistled softly. "Does it mean we get out?"

"If the place is sold to the wrong party, it does. I'll be selling from a pushcart and sleeping in an ashcan, the way you can't rent anything this side of hell right now."

"One way to be sure it goes to the right party." Mrs. Marsan paused for emphasis. "Buy it yourself."

Sig snickered. "Thirty-five thousand. How about you?"

"Doc Kincaid's going to buy it."

Ruthie's hard little voice cut in like a knife. Her thin arms held Maxie, so big and fat that he almost blotted her out. Her father looked at her, his shortsighted eyes behind their glasses waiting catlike to catch what she was going to let fly next.

"I heard him and Mr. Kennedy talking when I went after those digestion tablets you sent me for. Mr. Kennedy said the bank's tired of the trouble and wants to get rid of their real estate. He said they'll take ten thousand cash and the rest in notes, and Doc Kincaid says the building's not worth thirty-five, it's only worth thirty, and he'll pay five thousand cash and the rest out of the rents." Ruthie stopped for breath. "I listened hard and said what they said over and over till I learned it by heart."

Sig was stunned.

"How come you didn't tell me right away yesterday?"

"Because Mama said it would only make your indigestion worse."

"You see—" Sig spread out his hands gloomily. "I got the worst wash on the whole line."

"Mama says Uncle Benny's got five thousand and she's

got three thousand of her marriage money, so we won't starve no matter what happens."

"No," Sig admitted. "But where'll we *sleep?*"

"In Uncle Benny's basement."

"You can't do *business* in a basement."

"Uncle Benny did. He started his kosher shop in the basement."

"You're worrying too soon," Mrs. Marsan broke in. "The building's not sold yet."

"I still got to worry about my newsstand!" Sig contended.

Suddenly Mrs. Marsan knew what was strange about the store. The newsstand was gone from in front. At the same time the familiarity of the thing she saw the Bats dragging to the cellar on Wednesday evening was explained in a flash.

"I didn't miss it till today," Sig said, "because the weather's been too bad to put the papers out. I'm going to report it to the police."

"Now don't do that," Mrs. Marsan begged. "Don't be hasty. I know where the stand is. All you have to do is go get it. It's down in Doc's basement."

Sig's anger burned white.

"It is, is it." His calm was deadly.

"Not Doc Kincaid!—The boys took it."

"I see."

"All you have to do is go get it," Mrs. Marsan repeated uneasily.

"I'm not going to get it." Sig squeezed out the words, slow and hard, without moving his lips. After a moment he added, "When do they have their next meeting?"

"Tonight," Ruthie supplied promptly. "I know because Angelo's big brother Joe took the best gilt chair out of the beauty shop and Angelo told his mother and she bawled Joe out and made him bring it back. Duffy made a rule that every Bat who couldn't buy a campstool had to bring a chair from home so the audience could sit down."

Sig said, "They won't sit down long."

2

Coral Sands flew in to pay back five dollars she had borrowed two weeks before. Mrs. Marsan was just getting ready for a bath, and came out in her kimono with her head wrapped in a towel. The steam always upset her hair into damp springs, not unlike Lady's.

"I have to run." Coral had her hat and coat on. "It's eight already and I go on duty at nine. I just wanted to give you this before I made a mistake and gave it for a pair of nylons."

"How's the job?" Mrs. Marsan thought Coral looked a little tired.

"Well, hats aren't as heavy to handle as ice, but the iceman's line is probably just as hot. The hardest part of *my* labor is remembering which way to stretch my mouth at the customers—horizontal in a smile instead of vertical in a yawn." Coral took her vanity out of her bag and made sure her lips were right. "My patrons will be dining and dancing with their hats on if I don't shake a leg." She dropped the vanity back. "So long, and thanks again for the lift."

"You're welcome," Mrs. Marsan said.

As Coral turned to go, she nearly stumbled over Lady, standing behind her in a loggy daze. She caught back her balance and remained there frozen, while Lady looked at her steadily, without bothering to move.

"All right." There was a wry smile in Coral's voice. "So you're not going to let me pass. I get it."

Abruptly she turned to Mrs. Marsan.

"Listen, Marsie. Suppose you had something to do you

knew you ought to do and you couldn't make up your mind to do it. What would you do?"

Despite the trifling way the words were thrown together, Coral was never so serious. Her green eyes burned black.

"I don't know. Maybe—I guess I'd flip a coin," Mrs. Marsan decided.

Without speaking Coral took a nickel out of her purse and tossed it between the palms of her hands. Then she held them together in an attitude of prayer. The solemn set of her face was sincere. "Heads I do and tails I don't," she said softly. She lifted her right hand from the left and looked. "Heads." Her rouged lips curved into a characteristic one-cornered smile.

"So you do." Mrs. Marsan wondered what it was all about.

Coral looked at the Indian face on the nickel and shrugged. "History repeating. Redskin gets white woman's scalp."

"Well, it's cheap—getting your mind made up for five cents."

"Not as cheap as getting your heart made up at any price." Pensively Coral rolled the nickel between her fingers. "Marsie, I'm sorry. I'll have to borrow that fiver back again."

"Sure." Mrs. Marsan offered it.

"No. It's like this, Marsie. When my laundry comes, you take it and pay for it and keep it for me. I won't be here for a while."

"Atlantic City again?"

"Heaven don't happen twice. . . ." Coral waited a moment. "I'm going to spend some time with a girl friend of mine who has a room in the Village. It'll be nearer—I'll save carfare."

"That's nice." But not all there is to it.

"If you only knew how nice. . . ."

Mrs. Marsan had a puzzled feeling that bitter water ran under the thick ice of Coral's sarcasm. It was odd—Coral seemed older than when she first came in. She wriggled inside her coat as if getting herself together.

"Well, they'll be starting the bloodhounds after me if I don't get going. Thanks for everything, including the advice."

"No trouble," Mrs. Marsan said.

At the door Coral found she was still rolling the nickel between her fingers. She same back and snapped it down on the table with a tiny click that was like putting a period to a sentence.

"Buy Lady a candy bar. This is something between her and me. That nickel's got to be spent on her for the rhyme to come out right."

Mrs. Marsan wished she could take the lid off of Coral's head to see what was cooking inside. . . .

3

It was a relief to stretch out and let the hot water soak the soreness out of her tired body. The call on the minister had left the marks and bruises of a mortal struggle. Best shoes were the worst for feet used to slippers, and a corset was too radical a change from the customary kimono. Mrs. Marsan's ankles were swollen and the fat white flesh of her torso was ribbed red with the traces of whalebone.

The water gushed from both faucets and choked through the emergency drain, for tonight she was treating herself to a brimming tub. From time to time she turned on the shower lever with her foot, rolling over to let the spray scratch her back. The Niagara noise had the dual effect of soothing and stimulating her.

She stayed in the bath for more than an hour. Then she put on her pajamas and kimono, planning to sit out a good part of the night with a hot cup as a companion and Mr. Cernak's opera glasses. Saturday was always the climax of the week at the tavern. But Lady's behavior derailed her. Circling a spot crazily, Lady lay down in it only to get up almost at once and start the same procedure elsewhere. Mrs. Marsan concluded she wanted to be taken out. Lady's program had recently become somewhat erratic.

Coat and fascinator covered her negligée with the exception of blue flannelette legs. She got Lady into her sweater and harness.

At the head of the stairs she met Mr. Ingalls coming up. He was hatless and his light brown hair was blown over his forehead in a way that made him look like a boy. He nodded good evening to her over a rampart of library books.

"I've been lucky," he reported happily. "I've found an old history of Nebraska."

"That's fine," Mrs. Marsan said. "Tomorrow's Sunday and you can coop up and spend a nice time reading it." In her heart she did not think it nice at all. On a Sunday a young man like Mr. Ingalls ought to be out somewhere with his sweetheart.

"I'll wade through it tonight," Mr. Ingalls assured her. His assurance faded and he flushed. "I was wondering– Do you know–"

"Know what?" Mrs. Marsan encouraged.

"Do you know if Miss Larsch ever goes to the library? When she has books to return, I'd be glad to do it for her. She's so busy."

"Why don't you ask her?"

His color deepened.

"I never see her. I have to leave in the morning before she does, and I come home in the evening after she's gone. She's just as invisible on Sundays."

"I know. I was just saying at Joey Brent's the other day, you'd think she was chasing something."

"She is." Mr. Ingalls frowned.

"Is she? What?"

"I don't know. I can't make it out." He hesitated. "One day I caught her on the stairs and asked her to have dinner with me at the Hotel Pierre. I thought she'd like that. She said she was sorry—she had to keep after the Purple Emperor."

"The *Purple* Emperor?" Mrs. Marsan's hand went to her heart.

"Not literally," Mr. Ingalls hurried to say. "It's some poetic reference. The Purple Emperor, you know, is a rare moth. It's a prize all collectors go after." He glanced aside thoughtfully at the floor. "I've looked up every likely myth. . . ."

"Could she find it in South America?"

Mr. Ingalls raised his head.

"I don't know. I don't know anything about entomology. Why?"

"Because that's where she's going."

"Is she going away?" he asked quickly.

"In April."

"April. . . ." His misery showed. "That's soon."

"Two months. You could lug a lot of library books in two months."

"If she'd let me."

"Write her a note," Mrs. Marsan suggested, "and slip it under her door. That's what she told Edna Brent to do."

Mr. Ingalls brightened.

"I will. I never thought of that." Color flooded his face again. "I'm a stone when it comes to speaking, but on paper I can pour out my mind. It's just as if I had to have something to wrap my ideas up in."

"I guess that comes from working in the grocery business —wrapping things up all the time."

They turned to see who was coming up the stairs. It was Ruthie. Her face had the responsible air of a messenger who brings important news and her two short tight plaits stuck out behind in her hurry. She shot past them without a word, arriving at the Cernaks' door like a bullet at a target.

Jessamine opened. She held onto the knob for support, leaning against the doorframe. The green veil floated in a fantastic cloud around her neck and her magnificent burnished hair staggered in an uncertain psyche knot over her ear as she swayed. Jessamine's condition, as accurate as the calendar, indicated the beginning of the month.

"Mama sent me up to say your brother won't be home tonight. She thinks you ought to know." Ruthie's eyes measured Jessamine's disheveled beauty in happy horror.

"Very well," Jessamine said imperiously. "Send in the understudy. *Vesti la giubba!* The show must go on!"

"No." Ruthie was always careful to get things correct. She insisted on the same precision in others. "That's not it at all. Papa didn't mean for your brother to get caught, but the policemen took him off just the same with Doc Kincaid and Duffy. Papa went too, because he was the one who phoned in about what was going on."

"Excuse me." With an effort Jessamine drew herself up to her full majestic height. "In five minutes I'm going on myself. No interviews until after the performance!" She slammed the door.

Ruthie stood facing the blank wall for a moment bewildered, then turned on her heel and came away. Mr. Ingalls had been watching. He cleared his throat as if something had grown there that bothered him.

"She's sick," he said, his face queerly pained.

Ruthie stopped in her tracks.

"She's drunk," she corrected shortly.

"No." Mr. Ingalls' tone was firm and emphatic. "*She's sick.*"

"What ever happened?" Mrs. Marsan asked, her eyes like moons.

Ruthie's flat little chest expanded pompously. She smoothed back a wisp of wool that had loosened from the tight ripples of her hair, black and close as corduroy, like her mother's.

"Papa reported Doc Kincaid for holding public meetings in his cellar without a license. You can't do that. Especially *that kind* of meeting." Her mouth hardened. "It's against the government."

"Is that all?" Mr. Ingalls looked angry.

"No, it's not. Duffy stole Papa's newsstand for a stage to make speeches from. Duffy said he only borrowed it, and the first time, he went through one of the rotten planks, and he was going to give it back after he fixed it. But he's lying."

Mrs. Marsan's heart was ringing like an alarm bell. Next time Sig could find out for himself where his stand was. She wondered, choking:

"What did Mr. Cernak say?"

"He didn't know anything about the newsstand. He only knew about the chairs. He found that out when he came tonight and saw all the bedroom and dining room chairs. It was Duffy's Share-a-Chair plan."

"When did all this take place?" Mr. Ingalls demanded.

"You mean the raid? Only a while before you came in. There were five policemen in three cars."

"That's ridiculous!" Anger in a quiet man like Mr. Ingalls was an impressive spectacle. "Downright, deliberate, stupid damned nonsense!"

"Doc Kincaid won't think so." Ruthie challenged him with a satisfied smile. "And more than that," she started downstairs with her head in the air, "he's stuck with all those peanut chews—because the police aren't going to let the boys meet there any more."

"I told him." Mr. Ingalls looked suddenly defensive behind his bulwark of books. "I told him the last time. Saving society is the dreamer's most dangerous dream. I even said to him, 'Don't you know what happened to the greatest man ever lived who tried to make the world an ideal place to live in?' "

Mrs. Marsan was confused. She did not follow Mr. Ingalls very well.

"What happened?" She felt a trifle dizzy.

"He was crucified," Mr. Ingalls said.

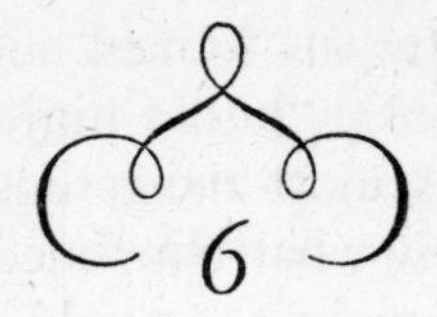

It was Sig who was booked on a serious charge.

Wednesday morning, going down later than usual for her paper, Mrs. Marsan found Hannah in a state verging on hysteria. Sig was gone. Hannah could only repeat the single fact of his departure, crying too brokenly to give details. Ruthie stood there, rocking Max in her arms, refusing to speak. "Uncle Benny will pay the fine and get Papa out" was all she would say.

Mrs. Marsan put down the two cents for her paper, retaining with disappointment the two dollars she had intended to place at the Fair Grounds. She knew the druggist and Mr. Cernak had been released, piecing the story together from bits she had collected from them themselves, and from Mr. Ingalls, during the last forty-eight hours. Apparently the whole matter had been dismissed for lack of evidence.

Duffy, it seemed, said the Bats were only allowing Sig to *share* the stand, according to the plan of the new world order. In answer to the next question, he confessed he recognized the advisability of consulting Sig about his willingness to share, but Sig, he said, was at supper, and the stand had to be readied to serve as speaker's platform at seven; the Bats had bought red, white and blue paper to cover it with from Doc. The next thing to be proved was whether the vast assortment of chairs in the cellar was shared with or without consent of the owners, or, a fact more familiar to the law, simply stolen. The parents identified and retrieved their chairs and the boys were acquitted of theft; what their sentence should be was left to the discretion of domestic authority. There was also the question as to whether property left on the sidewalk was public or private. In the end Duffy was ordered to return the stand in good repair.

What saved Doc from a fine was the fact that he received no rent for the cellar. Further, he attended none of the meetings. As far as he understood, he said, the place was used only as a gym. He admitted having seen the stand going down to the cellar, but he claimed he thought the boys had permission. Doc was admonished henceforth to keep his cellar to himself and the boys were forbidden to go near it.

It was Mr. Cernak who fared worst, for while no evidence of subversive literature such as pamphlets or incriminating printed matter was found in the investigation, Mr. Cernak welcomed his propinquity to the law as a chance to throw mud in its face. He brought out a newspaper clipping and orated vociferously on the defense of a man who had removed—he refused to say stolen—a dozen fur coats from a Park Avenue apartment; he insisted that the woman whose coats they were should be jailed, and the man who relieved her of them given a medal. The real crime, he claimed, was in having twelve fur coats while eleven people somewhere froze to death. The previous counts against Mr. Cernak for contempt of court and contributing to juvenile delinquency were brought up, and it was due only to Mr. Ingalls' testimony, as witness to Mr. Cernak's character, that he came out clear without a penalty of any sort beyond the severe injunction that the next time he would not be so lucky.

The latest development fitted nowhere into the case. Sig's part in it had suffered a sudden reversal of rôle. It was impossible to get anything more out of Hannah than tears and useless to question Ruthie. When Ruthie made up her mind not to tell anything she was as inexorable as when she made up her mind to tell everything.

Mrs. Marsan hurried over to the drugstore and was glad to see Doc Kincaid alone. She knew from experience that Doc would not stand around and talk. He said time was money and it ought to be spent in the same way—with intelligence. By intelligence Doc meant doing things that would save money or make more. Mrs. Marsan agreed that time was money, but she thought both should be spent for pleasure. Now she was figuring how she could part with a portion of her two dollars in a way that was at once practical and pleasant, to please Doc and herself. She had to make him feel he was not throwing away time talking to her.

"Give me a chocolate malted with egg," she ordered. That took a while to fix. Not to lose a second, she asked at once: "What's up with Sig?"

"The jig's up with Sig." Doc shot a brown stream into the silver shaker. "He's finding a muddy track and rough going trying to explain what they've got on him. He's in on a losing race this time, all right."

"What?" Mrs. Marsan reached blindly for Doc's meaning.

"He's up before Gamblers Court—that's what." He broke an egg as if he were cracking an enemy's head. "He'll have lots of leisure now to perfect that scientific system he was always working on—in jail. Unless he can come across with the five hundred fine." Doc stirred the drink vigorously and set it on the counter.

"Five hundred *dollars?*"

"Unless the judge insists on doughnuts." He gave Mrs. Marsan her change. "They got him red-handed. Racing forms, records and all."

"When?" Mrs. Marsan strawed the chocolate malted with

less enthusiasm than usual. She had just come from a hearty breakfast embellished with bacon.

"This morning. They were here as soon as he opened up. Plainclothesmen. Two of them. They were right on the scene when the paper man placed a bet. His telephones are coming out, too," Doc said with satisfaction. "He was using them for bookmaking."

Mrs. Marsan pushed the last of her drink away. It had no flavor at all.

"The police didn't know a thing." She saw ahead an equally flavorless stretch of days, devoid of the distant thrilling thunder of horses. "Donegan didn't have the least idea." She considered, frowning. "Somebody must have tipped them off."

"*I* did." Doc picked up her glass and put it under the counter, laughing quietly. "He thought he was getting *me*, didn't he. Well, did you ever hear of a wooden weapon used by the natives of Australia called a boomerang?"

The postman came in with a handful of mail. Doc snarled "Bills," and went to meet him.

2

Though it was too soon to expect an answer from Eric Arnold, Mrs. Marsan looked in Jean's box just the same. It was as empty as her own, except that it seemed to be filled with an air of anticipation that was almost visible whereas Mrs. Marsan's wore the face of resignation. While she was at it she exercised her habit of peering in all the boxes. When you had no mail of your own the next best thing was other people's.

There was a long fat-looking envelope from the Library of Congress for Mr. Ingalls. A Calendar of Events from the Metropolitan Museum for Adrian Larsch. Mr. Cernak's newspaper, *The Workers' Weekly*. A square that looked as if it might enclose a card for—it was for Joey Brent. That was nice . . . I wonder who. . . . Only a couple for Coral Sands instead of her usual stacks. . . . And in the Villars' box a blue oblong—

Mrs. Marsan was fascinated by the blue oblong. It was directed in a woman's hand to Burt, scratched up with penciled notations and purpled with rubber stamps. She bent over and squinted more closely through the small glass window. The original address had been lined out, and another —some exporting company—written in underneath in heavy masculine script. A wave of red ink ran through that. The other addresses were too dim to decipher, but Mrs. Marsan guessed they were an accurate list of the various places where Burt had sometime worked. She itched to know from whom the letter was. Taking a hairpin out of her knot she straightened it and inserted it in the slot. The letter turned over lazily. Another rubber stamp instructed "Return to Sender" and a tiny dirty hand pointed to the flap and the sender's name. Vivien.

Speaking of angels. . . . Mrs. Marsan was so absorbed that she barely had time to straighten before a figure came into view on the stairs. Vivien looked worried, unaware of anybody till she reached the bottom.

"You're getting off pretty late this morning, ain't you?" The ungenteel contraction slipped out of Mrs. Marsan's guilty embarrassment. She stood against the mailboxes, her breadth covering them, fumbling the tortured hairpin behind her back.

Vivien brushed by on an impulse to ignore her. Then she stopped as if a hand had been laid on her arm and turned around, still cold, but with a painful purpose leaning out of her face.

"It seems," she said deliberately, "that there have been

some malicious rumors grapevining around here. I thought you would be interested to know they are utterly untrue."

"Rumors?" A flutter as of pigeons had begun inside Mrs. Marsan. "I don't know—"

"You know perfectly well what I mean. I want them corrected."

"There must be some mistake. . . ." Mrs. Marsan quailed before this new woman whose tired brown eyes could be hard and glittering. Vivien was like a tiger cat, standing in sturdy defense of her lair.

"There is—a *vast* mistake. I'm glad you recognize it."

Cupid's sure got cataracts on both his eyes. . . . But the blind see a kind of beauty which the seeing can never know, and so it is the seeing who actually live in pitiful blindness. . . . Mrs. Marsan struggled to word what she felt but the result was only a merry-go-round that got nowhere. . . .

"It's a misunderstanding all around, I guess," she said heartily. "Maybe the best way to correct it is the way you cure the blues—forget it."

"We'll do that," Vivien agreed. "At the same time remembering not to let it happen again."

"Of course. I'm glad you spoke about it. It's the best way to iron things out."

Vivien relaxed and softened. She drew on her gloves and was about to go when she hesitated.

"I wouldn't want Burt to get wind of any such talk. He'd be furious. He's not well lately. He's always nervous when he's out of work." The anxious look came back. "He didn't sleep all night, except for a couple of hours from dawn to nine. That's why I'm late. I didn't want to waken him. I stayed to fix him a hot breakfast."

"Don't worry about him not sleeping if he took breakfast all right. If ever a man can't eat—that's the time to start worrying."

"Oh, I'm not worrying," Vivien lied gallantly. "I know it's foolish. Look at the way I worried after the holidays when he didn't come back and I didn't hear from him. Just as I thought, by the time he got around to answering he was ready to come home."

The hairpin behind Mrs. Marsan's back suddenly felt as hot to heı fingers as a live poker.

"Did he say," she had to ask it, "he got the letter?"

"Oh, yes." Vivien smiled. "We laughed about my remembering his brother's address."

"You'll be missing the next bus," Mrs. Marsan advised. "You better go."

Vivien said good-by and hurried off.

Burt would find the returned letter now, when later he came down on his way out. And the serpent in Vivien's poor paradise was scotched if not killed. But perhaps if Mrs. Marsan had not been there, blotting out the boxes— It was strange, she considered, how often and how close people probably came to their destinies, and what odd trifles—like a hairpin, for instance—deflected, or at least delayed, the hour. . . .

3

The card for Joey was from Phil Cassidy. He had made it himself, drawing a coy poodle up in the corner for which Lady Hamilton was beyond the shadow of a kink the model. Around the unique tail, with its falling fountain of long hair at the tip, there was tied a piece of real twine so heavy that it gave the effect of rope—in an obvious effort for the greatest emphasis. In the dazzling red letters of a headline Phil had printed: "To remind the Lady of Shalott she has a date to go walking today at three o'clock."

"How did he get that string tied on there?" Mrs. Marsan beamed on Phil's art as Joey held it up.

"He made two holes alongside the tail and drew it in from the other side."

"That young man's full of ideas," Mrs. Marsan approved.

"That what I think." Pearl narrowed one eye wisely. "I see ideas dropping out of him all over when he shake hands good-by with Miss Joey last time."

"Hush up, Pearl." Joey's round cheeks flushed ripe as an apple. "Don't you need a string to remind you of that date you have to clean up the Villars'?"

"No strings tied to *me*," Pearl grinned. "I calculate to be fast, free and fancy."

"Well, you'd better practice being fast getting over to the Villars'."

"Want to get rid of me." Pearl winked. "Where that note Miss Edna leave for Larsch? I slip it under while I'm at it."

"There on the bookcase."

"What's the note say?" Mrs. Marsan asked promptly.

"Her booking's been made. She leaves the first of April."

"April fool," Pearl snickered.

"I found out what she's after," Mrs. Marsan confided. "The Purple Emperor. It's a moth or a myth or something."

Joey laughed.

"No, it's not. It's a man."

"Ah-hah . . ." Mrs. Marsan drew the exclamation out into a song, wagging her head. Suddenly she asked with a snap: "How do you know?"

Pearl, having fetched her rubber gloves from the kitchen and covered her coiffure with an oilskin snood, returned to listen.

"One night late—they thought I was sleeping—I heard her and Edna talking. They were talking about getting married. Miss Larsch said she was waiting because she wanted a man who was a painter or musician or author or something—somebody interested in the fine things of life."

"Ha!" When Pearl guffawed the gleam of gold molars added to the magnitude of the effect. "If a man a *man,* don't matter what else he be."

Joey ignored Pearl.

"And Miss Larsch calls her ideal the Purple Emperor. Edna told her she was sure she'd find him because she had such rare gifts to offer—her wonderful intellect and her good looks. And Miss Larsch said yes, even her virginity—she'd been very careful to keep that."

"My God! . . ." Pearl muttered. "What Miss Edna say about getting married? She got nice looks if she touch them up and she not thirty yet."

"She said she never married because—" Joey bit her lip. "Because of me."

The loud silence that rose was scattered by the bell ringing. Lady jumped out of a sleep to bark.

"Go press the buzzer, Pearl." Joey's cheeks were apple skin again. "I've talked my lips off." She took a vanity and rouge stick out of her jacket pocket and expertly printed on her mouth.

"The only women who dared that when *I* was nineteen," Mrs. Marsan sighed, "were the bad women. Red lips and red lights went together."

"The world improved since then." Pearl's flame lacquered fingernails were so long she had to press the button with the ball of her thumb. "Now it red *hot* lips and *no* lights."

Their gay talk came to Mrs. Marsan in the kitchen, where she was fixing sandwiches and brewing coffee.

"That's fine—wonderful!" Phil applauded. "You're learning by leaps and bounds."

"Does that mean I move like a kangaroo?" Joey laughed joyously, like a child at a new game.

"That means you're getting somewhere. And getting somewhere is just one step from going places." Phil thumped over to her. "Let me give you a tip. Don't carry the horses. Let them carry *you*. You're a little too rigid. Just relax."

"How's this?"

"More like it. Now imagine you're a rambling rose leaning on a trellis."

"I'm going to ramble over to the bookcase."

"Good. I'll meet you there." His clumping steps sounded on the carpet. "Come on now. Slow but sure . . . 'She left the web, she left the loom, she made three paces thro' the room.' . . ."

Joey labored toward him.

" 'She saw the water-lily bloom, she saw the helmet and the plume—' " She laughed, and in her moment of incaution, lost her balance.

Leaning against the bookcase, he caught her in his arms. Mrs. Marsan could see them from where she stood by the stove. Joey had not let go her crutches, and she fell against him the way a wind-blown leaf strikes the trunk of a tree. For half a minute neither of them said anything. Joey looked up at him, embarrassed and breathless. Only the scarred side of his face was visible to Mrs. Marsan, but as he smiled down at Joey the raggedness of the seam was erased.

"Joey, what do you say—" A whimsical quietness softened his voice. "Let's change the ending of that poem."

"How?" Joey sounded little and far away.

"Come down to Camelot with me and let's do the town together."

For a moment Joey was silent as if his earnestness disturbed her. She tried to be casual when she said, "All right. But I'll have to do better than this or I'll be bumping into the 'magic sights' and smashing them."

She stirred in his arms to readjust her weight to her crutches and he helped her erect.

"You'd better rest now. It's not good to try too much the first time. You get tired and begin to make mistakes and then you get the notion it's all no use and old man Can't-do steps in. He's a crank you have to watch out for. When he turns up, crack him over the head with a crutch. Then walk all over him."

"Either I break his neck or mine."

"That's the spirit. And practice every day—half-hour at first, working up gradually. And remember what I said about falling. When you feel yourself going, don't crash—crumple." He added: "You fell very nicely this afternoon. . . ."

Mrs. Marsan waited another ten minutes to see if they had any more ideas about the ending for the poem. When their conversation turned to the weather, she decided it was all right to wheel in the tea wagon with its cargo of coffee, sandwiches and cake. Joey's blue set on the white napery looked nice, she thought. Not as genteel as the hand-painted Haviland, as she called it since the magnificent moment of Adrian's expert scrutiny, but kind of neat and cozy. . . .

Pearl came back sooner than expected in a noisy huff. She slammed the door, slapped the kitchen closets shut, mumbled a continuous stream of sulphuric epithets. Mrs. Marsan got up and went after her.

"For heaven's sake, Pearl. . . ."

"That rundown heel got a lousy hell of a lot of gut to put me out—"

"Sh . . . Miss Joey is entertaining, Pearl."

"Shush my behind. He—"

"*Pearl!*" An iron hand grabbed Mrs. Marsan's heart and squeezed it dry. She leaned against the edge of the sink and waited for the spasm to pass.

Pearl was frightened. The storm went out of her and she excused herself sheepishly: "He get on *my* nerves too."

"Who?"

"Mr. Burt. He say my slopping around make him nervous. It's him make *me* nervous. Walking up and down and getting in my way and dropping ashes all over where I just clean up."

"Did he pay you?" A soreness remained in her chest. Mrs. Marsan rubbed it without thinking.

"Sure. I find my money in Miss Vivien's desk drawer where she always leave it."

"Then what are you fussing about. You got the same pay for half the work."

"But I didn't get to use Miss Vivien's almond meal. I miss my facial—with him all around like a stink."

Mrs. Marsan remembered the letter downstairs.

"He's not going out today?" she asked anxiously.

"Don't look like. He not shaved nor nothing. All he do is smoke and stomp around. He act like crazy."

It was five by the kitchen clock. In another hour Vivien would be home. I'd better tell him, Mrs. Marsan thought.

She crossed the hall and knocked several times before Burt answered. Pearl was right. He looked a wreck.

"There's a letter for you in your box since morning. I thought you'd like to know," Mrs. Marsan said. "It looks like from a lady," she added carefully.

Burt's dead face came to life.

"Thanks. Thanks a lot." His fingers trembled tying the sash of his lounging robe. "I'll go right down."

At the head of the stairs he came face to face with Vivien.

"I came earlier," she said dully, "thinking you'd need—"

The sentence went unfinished. Vivien rested against the railing, as if she had no strength to get up the last step. She looked haggard, her cheeks gray and hollow. Mrs. Marsan's eyes sniffed at her hand, half hidden behind her back. The corner of a blue envelope stuck out of Vivien's clenched fist like a crushed wing.

4

After supper Jean came over of her own accord. That had never happened before.

"I have a letter from Mr. Arnold," she said, sitting down.

"Well! What do you know!" Jean's box was certainly empty this morning when she looked. The letter must have come this afternoon.

"I was surprised to get such a quick answer."

"Air mail's so fast it takes your breath away!" Eric must have held her letter to read in one hand while he answered with the other. It looked good. Everything was swimming—*swell!*—she added superlatively.

"He sent a snapshot." Jean went into her pocket after the buff envelope.

"You don't *say!*"

Mrs. Marsan's face glowed like a lantern. It seemed an hour before Jean extracted the letter.

"That's he on the left," Jean indicated.

The lantern darkened. The snapshot was sharp and clear. It showed two men, a tall blond somewhere under thirty and a shorter, heavier man with a mustache, forty-five at least. Their heads were uncovered, and the older man's hair—what there was of it—showed gray. Mrs. Marsan absorbed the details swiftly, holding the photo to the light.

"Is that him? With the mustache? Are you sure?"

"Of course." Jean sounded mildly surprised. "I'm positive."

"Maybe you read it wrong," Mrs. Marsan hoped. "Look at the letter again. What does it say?"

Jean found the place.

" 'I am enclosing a photo taken with my friend Dan,' "

she read, " 'who has been working in the same sector with me. As you see, he is quite a young chap, and I cannot help laughing him off with a *Phooey!*—as you say over there—when he claims the war has made an old man of him and soured the milk of his life. At his age a man should not be quarreling with the years. He should be making the most of them, as I'm sure you'll agree. I am perhaps telling tales out of school, but there is a local *mamselle* who would be more than willing to help him with the experiment. Dan has had a more difficult time than the rest of us, having lost his mother and sister in the London bombing. At any rate, here we are together, to greet you heartily.' "

"You don't have to read any further." Mrs. Marsan sighed from the soles of her feet. "The set way he writes, that's him."

"The whole letter is like that," Jean affirmed. "You can see it was written by a mature man. No nonsense. It's so sympathetic and understanding."

Mrs. Marsan no longer bothered how sympathetic or understanding it was. Or even sentimental.

"He expressed his regret about—my being a widow—so beautifully," Jean murmured. "I'll read it to you." Quietly she turned the page. " 'As well or better than anybody I know what it means, since I have all around me the unfortunate fact of women left alone in the world. In the case of those who are alone because their husbands are gone and their children frequently grown and married, at least they can say they have had their lives. Isn't that true? But among my friends here are also so many who suffer with hollow hearts that have never had their chance to be filled with memories and now are even empty of hope. So please think of these and try to be if only a little consoled.' " Jean paused and looked up. "There's something so gentle in those words. He must have a beautiful character, don't you think?"

Mrs. Marsan glanced at the photo again. "His *character* might be beautiful," she sniffed.

Jean folded the letter slowly.

"It's too bad Dan has a girl," Mrs. Marsan regretted. "Else you could drop *him* a line."

A silence fell into the room like a leaden weight, landing heavily, then utterly dead. Mrs. Marsan turned her eyes to Jean, half afraid to look. She sensed having said the wrong thing.

Jean's face was a mask of dismay and pale anguish. Her hand knotted in her lap, her body marbled.

"I wouldn't write to a younger man." The words came through her teeth, low and tense. "I wouldn't write at all if Mr. Arnold's letters weren't the way they are. I wouldn't answer them if they weren't more formal than friendly."

"Oh, I know what you mean!" Mrs. Marsan retreated. "Older men aren't so fresh. They know their place."

Eric's place was forever in Europe, so far as she cared. She looked at the picture one last indifferent time and passed it back to Jean, who slipped it with the letter into the envelope. She failed to offer Jean materials for answering right away.

"I have to go," Jean said. "I want to get out early in the morning to get a few things I've been needing."

Mrs. Marsan sighed once more. Eric Arnold. . . . Too bad Dan had a girl.

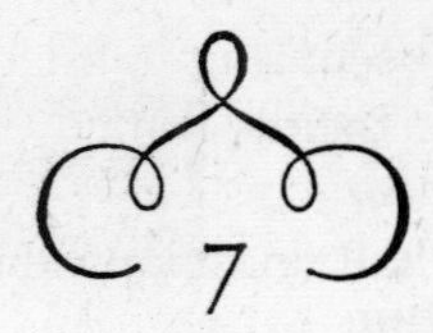

FOR MORE than a week Mrs. Marsan had been unable to sleep before dawn, coupling night and day with a short period of restless dozing. Insomnia bothered her no more than it ever did; she found the night hours as always mysterious and exciting, the dead street swarming with its own peculiar life. A man dropping a letter in the mailbox at three-thirty: what did he have to write that he sat up half the night writing it? A woman with her coat collar pulled up high against her face stepping into a taxi as day bleached the sky. And always the reeling, hilarious pattern of love and liquor behind the tavern. . . .

Your eyes are closed long enough, she always said, when you close them for the last time. So she used her wide-awakeness as a gift of extra living. The crime serial running in the newspaper was more deliciously horrible at three in the morning than at three in the afternoon, and the same food eaten at those respective hours had an entirely different flavor. She had no quarrel with her sleeplessness, none at all. What troubled her and left her with a heavy feeling akin to ache was the kind of dreams those brief snatches brought.

At first she dreamed of those around her. Mr. Ingalls went down a long row of empty sacks, filling them with shovelfuls of cereals and spaghetti. The sacks grew round and bloated, and in her dream Mrs. Marsan recognized them as the bellies of all the people Mr. Ingalls helped to fill over his counter every day from early to late. Then all the sacks merged together and collapsed, becoming a huge bottomless hole, on the brink of which Mr. Ingalls leaned on his shovel, sweating with despair. . . .

Or out of the fog of half consciousness she saw Vivien coming, gay and vivid as she had seen her the night before—an orchid tinseled to her silver fox, a gallant tilt to her shining head and her eyes brave and bright. And she would wake up with a start, wondering what was going on. . . . For it was no dream that Vivien and Burt went out together like lovers every night since the evening on the stairs, strange though this unexpected outcome was. It was no dream that Vivien came to her yesterday to ask about Sobel. "I want to borrow on these earrings. I'm a little short of the cash I need for a month in Florida with Burt, and I don't want to bother Marie Louise for a loan. She's giving me the month off—that's enough." Vivien was wearing the earrings, diamonds like petrified dewdrops.

Dreams of other people disturbed her meager rest, but they did not disturb her mind. It was the dreams of herself that followed into the next day, whispering at her elbow. She wondered why such things should float to the surface of her sleep when her thoughts had not stirred them for years.

She was young and slim again, walking down the lane that meandered back of the railroad station, with Louie's arm around her. It was summer and she could feel the richness of leaves and hear the tiny creakings and scrapings that were like the sound of things growing. She could almost smell the moonlight, a clean, cool smell like mint. They stopped in the shadows and Louis said, "I love you, Lily," and she put her arms up around his neck and he kissed her on the lips. Behind them the train went past with the rumbling of a giant drum, and suddenly her arms were empty and she was alone with the choking knowledge that the train had taken Louie away. . . .

All the next day she reviewed her dream, and remembered. She remembered the dress she wore that night. It was flowered dimity, reaching to the top of her high buttoned shoes. It was new since Easter and she looked pretty in it, with her chestnut hair down her back caught in a ribbon bow and her bangs ironed to a crisp curl. She and Louie made a pair, if she did say so herself. He was so handsome that it hurt yet to think of him. She saw him again, now, in his natty Sunday blue serge and high-standing collar with polka dot tie, his straw hat on one side of his dark head and his black mustache a thrill to behold. His brown eyes danced when his laugh made music. That was Louie—gay and dashing and let's-live-while-we-can.

Usually she dreamed of herself and Louie, but one night Henry came. He was handsome in a different way from Louie, as he was different from Louie in every other respect. This time she was standing with Henry, under an autumn tree, the leaves falling on their heads and shoulders like lazy rain. Henry rested his derby importantly on his arm and cleared his throat. She knew what he was going to say. "I want you for my wife, Lily." The declaration was very solemn and sincere, like Henry himself. She said, "Yes, Henry," and moved toward him. She felt on her cheek the neat horseshoe stickpin Henry wore in his quiet cravat as her head rested on his breast and he bent to kiss her hair. It was up in a psyche then, because she was three years older—nineteen.

All the next day she wondered how things would have turned out if she had married Louie instead of him. Less serene and secure—that was a certainty. She had been happy with Henry, but her life with him was like a graph that continues in a level line: there were no dizzy peaks of joy or steep depths of despair. With Louie there would have been movement, excitement, chance—misery sometimes, no doubt. With Henry she traveled the even road of safety. He took care of her; often he said, "I will *always* take care of you," and he made good his promise. But it was when she heard of Louie's death that she cried the hardest; perhaps not so much for him as for some part of herself that had died.

Suppose Ella had gotten Henry after all, and she had gone to Louie. . . . Where, what would she be now? One of those drab human mops that wash up the floors of banks and office buildings maybe? But who knew what colors many of such women saw beneath the suds and grime of their scrubbing in the gray hours of the night? . . .

Ideas like these trailed her with the heaviness of regret. That was unlike her. She scolded herself. She had a good life. No grudges against God—none whatsoever. . . .

Perhaps the recurrence of that griping pain around the heart had something to do with the way she felt mentally. It caught her off guard—when she was coming up with her paper, sitting at the table with her supper. She never went to the doctor unless discomfort drove her. The pain passed and she forgot it, until it came back again. It was Jean who said, "You ought to see Dr. Crowell. Come with me when I go on Saturday." Jean was surprisingly more alert, more alive lately. Was it the codliver capsules, or the buff-colored envelopes? Mrs. Marsan wondered, and worried a little too. . . .

Well, if she was going, as she promised, it was time to get dressed. When she opened the drawer for a pair of stockings, the jacket of Shaw, disguising *Tess*, looked at her with the hurt eyes of Mr. Cernak. For two Sundays the Cernaks had not come for afternoon coffee. Jessamine's failure she understood, but for Mr. Cernak it was the first absence in years. The reason came out of Sig, who was back since Hannah's brother paid his fine. "I told him how it was you squealed on the Bats about the newsstand. I got to explain why I got a right to get mad, don't I?"

Of late, getting into a dress wore her out. Suddenly she remembered something Phil had said: *Dreaming of the past is a sign of old age.*

Standing motionless for a minute, she could hear the years crawling up on her.

She brought Lady to Joey for keeping, not forgetting the leash so that Pearl could take her out if she showed symptoms. Lady's habits, like her figure, were changing. Her hours for airing had to be more elastic, just as her Christmas sweater had to stretch if it was to cover all of her steadily swelling dimensions.

Mrs. Marsan was not surprised to hear Phil Cassidy there. Amusing cards and messages came from his hand to Joey daily, and on St. Valentine's there had been roses and candy and a telegram. Phil was nothing if not thorough.

Pearl was no less thorough than Phil. For the last two evenings she had been bringing the flowers and the huge satin heart-box to Mrs. Marsan for shelter just before Edna came home. "I say to Miss Joey, if you going to surprise Miss Edna, you got to *surprise* her. You can't go letting the mew out of the bag ahead of the cat." Pearl rolled her eyes. "Jeez. It going to be *some* surprise. . . ."

This morning Pearl was in the kitchen brushing up roach cadavers into a dustpan.

"Edna putting down borax again?"

"No." Pearl emptied the pan into a paper bag. "Somebody around putting up a fight."

"What?"

"Somebody battling these bugs with poison. They been coming over here to croak. I been burying a new batch every half a hour."

"Don't let Lady get at them," Mrs. Marsan cautioned. "She's got so lazy she's not even interested in the live ones any more. But keep an eye to her anyhow."

"I keep a broom to her—she come interfering with my funerals," Pearl promised.

"Mrs. Marsan!" Joey called. "Come see Phil's leg. It's wonderful!"

She hurried into the living room, her curiosity bubbling.

Phil came to meet her without his crutches. The bandages were gone and he walked with a long, easy stride.

"Hello, Mrs. Marsan." He shook hands. "They peeled the bark off of me, you see. How does it look?"

"Simply grand!" Breathlessly Mrs. Marsan eyed him up and down. When she recovered she asked: "Since when?"

"Wednesday night. I could navigate under my own steam right away, but they made me do some practice runs before making my first port of call—out here."

"Well, what do you know! . . . They sure work wonders and work them fast these days."

"You see?" Phil turned to Joey. "You hear that, Joey? Now *you* do some work and the wonders will come."

"I get so darned tired," Joey sighed.

"As long as you don't get tired of trying. Remember, you can't stop when you haven't started yet."

"You've been doing fine," Mrs. Marsan encouraged.

"I'm mighty glad the doctors didn't tire of trying on that leg and foot." Phil looked down his side proudly. "When they began it was just one whopper of a wound. For a while it looked as if that pin and I were going to part company. Now it goes wherever I go."

"But you can't do that with the leg of a chair. You can't put life in wood."

"Peg-leg Peter Stuyvesant did," Phil insisted. "And believe me, that old boy got around plenty."

"Once I went to a spirit meeting where the chairs walked," Mrs. Marsan recalled.

Phil went silent, taken up with thought. He looked as if

he were considering something. He absorbed Joey, slumped in a chair with her crutches idle against the arm, and decided.

"Listen, Joey. There's life in everything. Ben Franklin pulled it out of the air—electricity. James Watt got it out of water—steam. Both are a means of moving far and fast. But without a lot of will and work nobody would be getting to the corner on them. It's like the rabbits in the hat. You've got to put them in first with the *idea* before you can pull them out and make magic."

Joey shrugged. "They were geniuses."

"I'm not a genius," Phil said. "Watch this." He held up his left hand and wiggled the gloved fingers realistically. "Wouldn't you think it was my own?"

Slowly he took off the glove and held out a rubber palm as true as flesh. Joey put her hand in it wonderingly and he curved the rubber fingers around hers.

"It's beautiful . . ." she whispered.

A strange look came to Phil's face.

"You don't think it's gruesome?"

"Gruesome!" Joey's voice came back. "I think it's glorious!"

"The first and last time I decided to show a girl my hand" —Phil twisted out a smile—"she fainted."

"It's more wonderful than real fingers." Mrs. Marsan's eyes were riveted to them. "Because you *expect* real fingers to wiggle."

"The word for it is cinetization," Phil said. "The muscular power left in an arm stump is harnessed to the mechanical hand by levers. Some of the fellows I know can typewrite, play piano and sculpt. The first thing I did with mine was punch Mr. Can't-do in the nose."

Joey fought to her feet and adjusted her crutches.

"I gave *in* for a while"—she tightened her lips—"but I didn't give *up*. You stay to lunch and I'll show you."

"All right. I'll phone Brenda from the drugstore. At the same time I'll say it's all right for her to come over Monday afternoon. By the way—" Phil turned to Mrs. Marsan. "Could you drop in a minute on Monday? I'd like you to meet my sister too."

Pearl appeared in the living room doorway, her chin trembling with panic.

"Mr. Phil staying to lunch we got to have lunch right away *now*," she announced.

"That's crazy, Pearl," Joey said. "We'll have it at one, as usual."

"Today *Saturday!*" Pearl shrieked.

"What in the world—" Joey stopped clumping around and turned to her. "*One o'clock*, Pearl," she repeated.

Mrs. Marsan wondered what had gotten into Pearl. Then it burst on her like a bomb. Edna. . . . Oh, my God. . . .

2

Mrs. Marsan and Jean lunched in town at an automat. Stoically Mrs. Marsan passed up the roast beef for the vegetables, the coffee for the milk; but in the pastries she withstood cream pie only to succumb to chocolate cake. The effect of Dr. Crowell's scolding always lasted until dessert of the first subsequent meal.

About some things he had been more emphatic than ever. Absolutely no stimulants. Absolutely no rich foods. Absolutely no strenuous exercise. Absolutely no excitement. She listened with respectful attention; but such a régime was to her a positive curse rather than a possible cure. She reasoned neatly that the pain endured only a minute or so, whereas the treatment was a sickness that continued around the clock. What she wanted was a prescription that could be filled at the drugstore. She was more pleased when Dr.

Crowell tore a page from his pad and said: "Keep these tablets with you always. Carry them around in your pocket or purse. At the very first indication of an anginal spasm slip one under your tongue."

Jean was eating dreamily, though she had chosen her lunch with an interest never evident before. She looked more substantial today. There was color to her face.

"What did he say—getting along all right?"

Jean came back with a start.

"Who?"

"The doctor."

"Oh, he said the blood test was fine. Just to keep on drinking lots of milk and taking the vitamins and not to bother to see him again until the end of March."

"Is that all he said?" Mrs. Marsan asked it because from the way the color warmed her cheeks it looked as if Jean had something tucked away in a secret pocket.

"Yes, that's all." Jean dived into her salad. She had a feeling that her thoughts were standing naked at a window and she struggled to curtain them with indifference.

She would not have known how to explain the experiences of the morning; they were like shadows around her, very real, but intangible, and their shapes puzzled and disturbed her. She shrank from talking about them, but thinking about them had an odd, piquing savor. . . .

First there was that suffocating stirring when the doctor, in placing the stethoscope, took her breast in his hand. She looked aside from her unbuttoned blouse, as if the stirring were something she could have seen had she wished. His hand was large and warm. She was conscious of a chill emptiness when it was gone. Perversely her heart began to run away and she could not catch it until he said, putting his hand on her knee, "Relax . . . just relax now. . . ." Even then. . . . She finally brought her heart to bay by counting carefully the shining instruments in the case against the wall.

Right now, again, she could feel the rich warm strength of his hand as if it were something she held in her own. She could feel it around her taut waist as for a moment on leaving he drew her against him and said: "Nothing wrong enough with you to worry about. A few more pounds and more people—and we'll be all right."

The other thing happened outside in the reception room when, alone, she was waiting for Mrs. Marsan. It was as if she had never seen the bronze of Herakles there before. She walked over to the table where it stood, a few curly-eared magazines beside it. The arm was drawn back from the emptied bow, muscles round and firm as stones. Her eyes passed to the hard bare chest, the indrawn pit of the stomach, down the frank freedom of the thighs. She could feel on her shoulder the weight of the hand jealously gripping the bow, and the parted lips and the eager eyes were searching not after the flown arrow but for her. When the door opened and somebody else came in she wheeled around with a swift sting of shame and returned to her chair, feeling sillier because she trembled.

"Are you *sure* that's all, dear?" Mrs. Marsan had been watching her for more than a minute.

"Oh, that and the same old thing—I should get out more—find something to do and meet people—get an int—" she dropped the word nervously and picked it up again—"interest in something. . . ."

"You didn't get any more letters from Eric Arnold, did you, dear?" There's *something* going on behind the scenes here. . . .

"Why, yes." Jean fumbled her paper napkin. It planed off to the floor. "I got three."

"*Three?*" Mrs. Marsan choked. She hated milk. "*When?*"

"Yesterday."

"I declare! I looked in your box right after the mail came and didn't see a thing." She closed her lips suddenly, knowing it was too late to lock the stable after the horse got out, but it passed Jean unnoticed.

"I was in Brinkmann's getting something when the postman came and he just handed me mine."

So that's how it happened. . . . "A lot of wonderful news?" she fished.

"Eric"—*Eric!*—"always writes a wonderful letter, but the news isn't very wonderful. He's quartered in a schoolhouse where there's no heat and they have no light after nine o'clock. He was writing by candle."

"Three letters by candle?" She recalled the snapshot. Eric was probably lonely.

"The other two weren't really letters. One was a set of views of Brussels and the other was a souvenir handkerchief with Belgian lace."

"Oh." After all, though Jean thought them wonderful, one of Eric's letters was enough. Mrs. Marsan found them as cold and bare as the classroom he bunked in. She asked hopefully: "Didn't he say anything about Dan?"

"Yes, indeed! Dan's married."

The chocolate cake went to dust in her mouth. She felt as she did at the end of the month when her last two dollars failed to pick a winner. Numbly she made room for the woman who came to take a place at their table. The automat was crowding with the midday mob.

For a moment she was paralyzed. Then she said irritably: "Now why couldn't it have been Eric!"

Jean's feathers ruffled. "Why *should* it be Eric!"

"Only because he's older," Mrs. Marsan covered. "Dan had time."

"Eric isn't old. . . ." Her mind started to work like a comptometer. He didn't look nearly so old as Dr. Crowell.

Would you say the doctor was about fifty? Fifty was mature, but not old. Then was forty or forty-odd old? His letters . . . so refined, so reserved, so full of character and intelligence and sympathy with his cheerless surroundings, but would you call them *old?*

"Age is how you take it—that's what I always say," the woman between them cut in. She was eating pie and drinking coffee. Mrs. Marsan became aware of her, enviously. "Darling"—the woman turned to Jean—"you're so beautiful I can't keep my eyes off of you. Is your hair natural?"

"Why, yes." Jean was embarrassed.

"I was saying to myself, she must be Swedish. You see that straight honey blond hair on Swedes. I bet your boy friend adores it."

"My husband did," Jean said softly. "I lost him in the war."

The woman made a sympathetic sound with her tongue like fast dripping water.

"That's all you hear. . . . Listen, darling. Take my advice. Get married again right away. Don't wait— You might wait too long. Look at me. God, if you knew how I hate living alone. You go to a show to forget it—you come back to your empty rooms and there it is twice as big as before. If you feel bad—nobody around to give you a comforting pat or even a cup of tea. Listen, darling. You're not unfaithful to the other, remarrying right away. It doesn't mean you've forgotten. On the contrary, it means you're remembering—because you want to be happy like that again." She turned to Mrs. Marsan. "Am I right?" she said.

Her words had fallen on Mrs. Marsan like a landslide, leaving her too deeply buried to answer. Instead Mrs. Marsan looked at Jean, fearful of what she would find. Jean's eyes were intent on the woman, without hurt or anger.

"Sometimes I get so lonely I just have got to go out of the

house before I go out of my mind. Look at me now. Know what I'm doing? Part-time clerking at Macy's. Kitchen department. Everything in elegant aluminum and agateware. It's fun. And you can't think of yourself while you're selling a flour-sifter."

"I'll have to do something like that," Jean said.

"Why don't you? They'd give *you* a job before you asked for it. Not in the basement, either. They'll want you where you'll show. Why not come along with me?" She finished her coffee and began drawing on her gloves. "I'll show you the ropes. I'm headed for my rolling-pins now." She got up and waited.

Mrs. Marsan worked her way back to words.

"You go along, dear."

"I'd better see you on the subway first. The steps—"

"I'll take the escalator. Doctor says I'm almost better enough to be all right anyhow."

She watched Jean and the woman through the door. What's on the other side of the door for Jean, I wonder? . . . Not the ugly empty rooms that woman was talking about. But not Eric, either . . . please, Jesus. . . .

3

She met Edna waiting for the bus home. It was two-thirty, barely time for Phil to have lunched and left. If she could keep Edna out until three, there would be a better chance of her missing him.

"Joey asked me to bring back some bananas. I'm sorry I couldn't find any," she told Edna.

"I thought she didn't like bananas," Edna said, puzzled. "Maybe I can find them around here somewhere."

Mrs. Marsan looked at Edna walking away. Attractive girl. . . . That new upsweep brought out reddish glints in her hair that went well with the pert plum-colored hat. A man turned to look at her.

Three blocks from home the bus halted in a traffic tangle, which was unknotting slowly under directions from a police whistle. The driver got out and came back to report there was a fire up the street and he would have to detour. Those who lived close enough left the bus and Mrs. Marsan with them.

She saw the bright red of the fire engines and the gathering of people impersonally at first but before she had gone half a block her heart thundered the truth at her. She tried to run. At once an iron ring clamped around her chest and held her back. All she could do was hurry, her mouth open greedily for air.

She pushed a place for herself in the crowd before the oil station. Her heart against her ribs was like the clapper of a frantic bell. She was unable to hear anything but its urgent clang. She leaned against one of the gas pumps, snapping at breath, her eyes raised to the spot in the roof gushing smoke and flame. Lady . . . *Lady!* . . . She must have screamed it because people stared at her and parted as she bore through them. *Lady!* A sharp loud bark answered. She looked around and found Pearl's face and remembered.

She was on the edge now. The street was a mess of python hose and machinery and ladders, policemen and shouting fire fighters. The activity centered before the drugstore, it rose and reached its climax at the Cernaks' apartment directly above. She could see men moving about in the living room, blue blobs in a gray mist.

"God's sake what happened? . . ."

"Some lush was spraying roaches. They think she must have dropped a match on the stuff."

"She's still up there," somebody behind her said. "She won't come down."

Attention froze on the bedroom window. Jessamine appeared, her hanging hair a fire in itself, her green veil frothing around her neck. She spread her superb arms, thrusting off the men who held her. Out of the confusion her voice rose, weird and wonderful, in the "Magic Fire" music, changing abruptly to the Walküre's battle cry as they tried to fasten her again. The crowd in the street stood spellbound. No one noticed the hugest of the firemen climbing the ladder to get her down, nor the thick smoke now creaming through the living room window next. A thin fog was spreading in the bedroom and Jessamine's wild call broke on a cough.

She refused to understand her danger or the efforts of her rescuers. She understood only what was trapped inside of her and everything external was a projection of it. She began to sing again, a different theme, swelling from tenderness to a burst of joyous passion. Her rage when the man at the top of the ladder interrupted her broke the spell of her voice and the people in the street began to laugh.

It was Mr. Ingalls who was shouting.

"Brünnehilde! It's Siegfried! *Siegfried*, Brünnehilde!"

He had no coat on and his hair fell over his forehead. Under his arm he hugged a thick block of his precious price lists.

"Here's that wacky guy again."

"He ran into the building for those papers against the police. He'll get something for that," the person behind Mrs. Marsan said.

"*Brünnehilde! It's the third act. Come down off the flaming mountain!*"

"I'm getting back to my truck before they start passing out the straitjackets." The big fellow left a hole at Mrs. Marsan's side that filled up immediately.

"Mr. Ingalls was always so quiet," she murmured.

Jessamine heard him. She looked with wakened eyes at the giant in the fireman's helmet and docilely allowed herself to be helped. Slowly they descended the ladder, his arm around her waist. When they reached the sidewalk the crowd cheered and applauded. Jessamine turned and bowed. She was radiant.

Convinced that nothing more could happen, the crowd raveled out. Mrs. Marsan found Pearl again, and Joey and Phil, with Lady in his arms.

She stopped short when she saw Edna. White and wide-eyed, Edna rushed toward them, hysterically clutching a large paper bag. When Joey saw her, she clumped forward eagerly, her face a sun.

"Look, Edna! I can walk!"

Panic screamed in Edna. "Don't—" She freed her hand and caught Joey. "Oh, God! . . . you'll fall. . . ."

The starch went out of Joey. She hung on her crutches limp and crumpled.

"Who got you down." Edna was hoarse. Anyone could see she was nearly crazy with fright.

"Phil." Joey gleamed again. "Phil carried me. I haven't learned the stairs yet."

"That's next." Phil smiled in that way of his which erased his scar.

"Phil's been teaching me." Joey moved to him and propping herself expertly, took his arm. "Every Wednesday afternoon—Edna, I wanted to surprise you!"

Edna looked from one to the other of them, saying nothing. A slow horror spoke from her eyes. *I've lost you . . . I've lost you more completely than if the fire—*

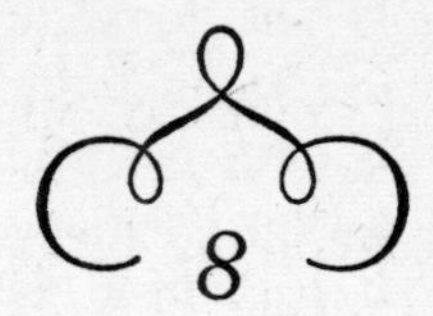

Coral Sands came back for her laundry.

The morning was white and cold. She took off her boots in the kitchen, where they ran little baths of melted snow. It was fur weather, yet she was wearing her spring coat, shapeless over her suit and a heavy sweater.

"What's the news, Marsie?" She went and stood by the radiator, where Lady was sleeping on a pillow. "It ought to be thick as dust in three weeks."

"Well, you near lost your laundry this time." Mrs. Marsan told her about the fire. "Jessamine stayed with me till they set her place to rights. They're still working on the kitchen roof. That's where most of the damage was."

"Where did the Hope of Humanity stay?"

"Who?"

"Mr. Share-the-Shekels."

"Oh. With Mr. Ingalls. I'm sure my sofa would have been nicer than Mr. Ingalls' canvas cot. And poor Mr. Ingalls slept on the floor. He's never gotten around to buying a bed, you know. He says he's been too busy. Did I tell you Mr. Cernak and me had a run-in?"

Coral shook her head. "I hope you shared hell with him."

"It was like this." Mrs. Marsan gave the details of the raid. "But as I explained to Mr. Cernak, when I told Sig where his newsstand was, I wasn't squealing on the Bats—I was trying to square them."

"You certainly succeeded." Coral's laugh was her first attempt at gaiety. "They were so squared I bet they felt framed."

"Mr. Cernak stopped coming for Sunday coffee. But he got over it. He said he thought he had a right to be offended, but he knew he had no right to *use* that right. He said *forgiving* was as important as giving. I thought that was nice. I wrote it down in my scrapbook."

"You should have engraved it and presented it to Sig as a consolation prize."

"Sig's been placing bets through his brother-in-law Ben Levine." She remembered sadly, "I owe Uncle Benny six dollars for bad horsemeat. . . ."

"I suppose Doc will claim a cut from the police on Sig's fine?" Coral said with a curl of the lip. Her mouth was less luscious today—somewhat drawn and forced-ripe.

"He's claiming all the gym stuff in his cellar—going to sell it to cover wear and tear, he says. And he's making big on the fire. The insurance company's got to pay him water damages on junk anybody else would have been *glad* to see burned. And then there're the repairs. The drugstore and the Cernaks' will be practically brand-new. He's lucky—he's going to buy the building, you know. He's the only one got enough money but he's haggling the price. Meantime he's passing out hints about six months' notices so people will lose sleep worrying they'll have to get out with nowhere to go."

Coral shrugged. "I can't stay here anyhow." She took out a cigarette, tapping the end on the case impatiently. "Don't tell me any more about that creeper. He upsets my stomach." She struck a match with her fingernail. "What's Joey Brent up to? When I stopped in to say hello just now she looked different. Stars in her eyes one minute and rain the next. It don't gibe."

"She's in love!" Mrs. Marsan headlined.

Coral exhaled with a sullen snort. "The jackass. . . ."

"Edna wants to take her away on a long trip. She's got her office dizzy working out a way to get Joey off somewhere so far she'll forget Phil ever existed."

"A woman is a jackass to love any man. But she's two jackasses to give him up." Coral walked over to the table and stamped her cigarette out in Mrs. Marsan's pink glass bowl. "Between the one and the other it hurts less to keep the guy."

"You know Joey. She won't even hurt a roach. She don't care how she gets hurt herself—she don't want to hurt Edna."

"If there's anything I hate," Coral said viciously, "it's these damn drooling dramas of love and duty!" She went back by the radiator. "Just hate something hard enough and you'll find yourself handcuffed to it," she added, annoyed.

Coral's not looking well, Mrs. Marsan thought. She's as jumpy as springs and there's no spark to her eyes.

"How about a good cup of coffee to tone you up?" she suggested. "I have some on tap. Like some with a couple of doughnuts?"

Coral smiled. "Marsie, there are times when your mind-reading is actually unobjectionable."

Mrs. Marsan kept on retailing the news while she brought in the tray with the jumbo cups.

"Jean's got a job, selling costume jewelry at Macy's." She said nothing about the correspondence with Eric Arnold because it left a green persimmon taste in her mouth. "All they have to do to clear an item off the counter is hang a sample of it on her. She's getting salary and commission." She returned to the kitchen. "There's something awfully funny lately about Mr. Ingalls. I used to notice the light under his door until two or three in the morning, and now it's out at eleven. Don't you think that's funny?" She came in and set a plate of doughnuts on the table.

"I don't know. Maybe he decided to cut down his light bills."

"No. It's funny. And he was so strange the other day. You know, he wants to build something. I feel so sorry for him. He'll never build anything selling groceries. So I said—I just felt I had to say something when I picked up my bag—I said, 'Never mind, Mr. Ingalls. You can build *people*.' And he said, 'Oh, God!' and crossed his fingers."

"That's the way I feel about hats." Coral sat down on the sofa. "When I see another one coming I say 'Oh, God!' and my eyes cross."

"I got to thinking about the Sunday I went to bring him some coffee. His place was so upset I asked him how he stood it and he just laughed and said, 'Once in it I never notice it.' A remark like that don't make sense." She filled Coral's cup. "I'm wondering if the poor fellow's losing his mind. . . ."

"He always was crazy"—Coral took a doughnut—"over that Larsch woman."

"Adrian's going on a trip. In April."

"How are the folks next door to her?" The inquiry was too casual not to be forced.

"Who? Oh, the Villars." I might as well tell her. Maybe she ought to know. "They're getting along fine. They go out together every night and Vivien's treating Burt to a month South."

"The travel tick's bitten everybody around here." Coral tried to sound unconcerned, but she put her doughnut down as if the sheer sight of it choked her.

Quickly Mrs. Marsan changed the subject.

"Tell me something about yourself. How's the model business?"

"That." Her mouth twisted. "I've turned it over to the Department of Sanitation."

"What?"

"It stinks," Coral explained.

The fragrance of food roused Lady. She got up heavily and lumbered over to the sofa. Coral looked at her, bloated with waiting lumps of life. She watched Lady chewing drowsily, like an old cow, the pieces Mrs. Marsan gave her.

"Listen, Marsie." Coral turned on her with such suddenness that Mrs. Marsan jumped slightly and the coffee washed over the side of her cup. "I want to borrow those opera glasses to get some money on them."

"How much do you need." Mrs. Marsan steadied. "It's near the end of the month but if it's not too much—"

"I sold my leopard to my girl friend for the bulk, but I need fifty dollars more."

"What is it you want this time?"

"It's something I *don't* want!" Coral said fiercely.

Her green eyes drilled into Mrs. Marsan's for a moment, then dropped on Lady with repugnance. For a while there was silence. Mrs. Marsan placed her cup and saucer on the table with a shaking hand. Putting two and two together made a four that struck her speechless.

"Atlantic City. . . ." Coral's smile was bittersweet.

"Don't be crazy." Mrs. Marsan sounded to herself like somebody else. "You don't want those opera glasses."

"I don't want a baby, either."

"Why not?"

"Don't be an ass!" Coral snapped. "On the contrary, *why*?"

"Funny thing about women." Mrs. Marsan shook her head. "If they can't have any they break their necks trying to. And if they *can* have them, they break their necks trying not to. I tried everything under the sun to have one."

"I can't support myself," Coral said sullenly.

"Couldn't you go home? Where're you from?"

"Pleasant Lake, Indiana." She laughed shortly. "Pleasant Lake was never much good to me before. But I might find a use for it now. I might go back and jump in it."

"You can save train fare jumping in the Hudson River," Mrs. Marsan said, "if you're fool enough."

"Let's have those opera glasses, Marsie. I've got to run along."

"No." Mrs. Marsan was firm. "Not for that."

"If you think you're being moral you're a damn fool, Marsie." Coral looked at her steadily. "You know I can get the money."

Mrs. Marsan sighed. "It's remarkable how much trouble people will go to to get themselves into it," she said.

Coral left without finishing her coffee. In the hall she stopped dead at the sight of two suitcases before the Villars' apartment. The door was ajar and she could hear long nervous strides covering the rooms inside. She made a step forward, hesitated. Then, hugging her laundry bundle, she raced down the stairs.

2

Mr. Cernak came to fetch a few articles stored with Mrs. Marsan while the repairs were in progress. Jessamine was with him. She followed him like a great St. Bernard, unable to help for the shaking of her hands, mute in her end-of-the-month misery. Every few minutes she quivered from head to foot with chills, though Sig had the building summer warm.

"You put on this sweater," Mrs. Marsan said. She had taken it off early in the evening because she was perspiring.

Jessamine let herself be helped into the shapeless sack like a child. The sleeves were too short but the shoulders were wide and friendly. She crossed her arms and hugged them.

"It reminds me of the shawl I wore as Mimi. The roofs of Paris are covered with snow, and in Rudolph's garret the fireplace is bare. I drop my key, and as we grope for it in the dark, Rudolph touches my hand and sings *Che gelida manina. . . .*"

"Come now, Jessie," Mr. Cernak persuaded. "Sit down on the sofa and rest. You must try to rest a little."

Jessamine sat down obediently. She thrust her hands in the pockets and drew out a small brown bottle. Her fingers convulsed around it.

"Those are my nitroglycerin tablets," Mrs. Marsan said. "Just put them down on the table."

"Medicine. . . ." Jessamine put it down with tenderness.

"Yes. When I get one of those awful pains I just slip a tablet under my tongue and sit still till it passes."

"It cures you . . ." Jessamine said in wonder. She fell back, staring at the bottle entranced.

Mr. Cernak had gone off with an armful and was now back for another.

"Things like this should be done in the daytime," he said. He was in his shirtsleeves and his suspenders were black and startling against his skinny chest. "I shouldn't be breaking up a neighbor's evening hours. But with that jailer of a job I have—"

"I don't mind it a bit," Mrs. Marsan assured him heartily.

Mr. Cernak put down the Dresden vase which had been presented to Jessamine in Saxony. He straightened, and with calm deliberation smoothed down the fronds of gray hair that always spread obliquely across his forehead.

"Precisely. You don't mind it a bit. And it's because others like you don't mind it a bit that mankind is in the mess it's in. Nothing will be corrected if nobody cares!"

"I didn't mean—" Mrs. Marsan began.

"Accumulated money is committed murder, my dear madam. Every dollar the drone spends is a drop of some slave's blood. Every unworked-for meal is the flesh of a fellow-man." Mr. Cernak raised his twig of an arm and shook an angry forefinger. "Capitalism is *cannibalism!*"

Mrs. Marsan said "Oh!" and shuddered.

"From you idle rich we want our share of leisure. Learning. Decent living. What do we get when we ask for the bread of brotherhood? The stones of selfishness." His blue eyes flared like the windows of a furnace. "At the Metropolitan Opera House yesterday I tried to buy tickets for my sister and me. I thought the music might be a tonic for her nerves. Could I pay the price from my threadbare pockets? No! While the leeches of society cart their jewels in limousines to the Diamond Horseshoe!"

Jessamine sat up. "We don't go to the opera?"

"Not until we smash the existing order of inequality, my dear!" He looked at her and the furnace fires died down. "Don't worry now, Jessie. Everything will be all right. Look, Jessie. Just remember this sign." He held up both hands with the thumbs tucked in. "Micah, 4:4: 'But they shall sit every man under his vine and under his fig-tree; and none shall make them afraid.' "

"Lots of bosses are fine people," Mrs. Marsan defended. "Look at Marie Louise. She gives Vivien Villars everything she asks for. Now it's a month off with pay, so Vivien and Burt can go to Florida. They left today."

"They didn't," Mr. Cernak objected. "I just saw her dragging in from work, and she looked half dead."

"I saw Burt leave with the suitcases, with my own eyes."

"*She* didn't," Mr. Cernak insisted. He picked up the vase again and marched off with it.

"We can't go to the opera under the existing order," Jessamine moaned.

3

As soon as the Cernaks left, Mrs. Marsan knocked at Vivien's door.

"I thought I'd see how you made out with Sobel," she apologized. "About the earrings, you know."

Vivien's pink moiré housecoat was only half buttoned, as if she had been interrupted in the act of dressing and forgotten to finish. The bloom it was intended to lend to fading skin tried bravely and failed. Vivien looked gray, almost livid.

She said "Come in" from habit, without life.

"Did he give you all you wanted?" Mrs. Marsan began again.

Vivien sank into a chair, her hands dead in her lap.

"He offered to buy them at more than I paid. Good diamonds are that scarce. I only wanted a loan"—she was staring straight ahead—"but I guess I'll sell them now."

"Decided on staying South more than a month?"

"The Florida trip is off."

"You mean"—Mrs. Marsan squinted—"you're planning some place else?"

"Burt's gone," Vivien said tonelessly.

"For long?"

"He won't come back this time."

Mrs. Marsan stared at her aghast. "Where did he go?" she asked in a whisper.

"Detroit—" Vivien's colorless lips forced a smile "—so he says. . . ."

"He let you know?" Burt hurrying off in a taxi this afternoon. . . .

"He left me a note. I found it on my vanity when I sat down to fix my hair." Vivien looked like a corpse. Her face in the shadow of the lamp was ashes. "A very nice note. . . . He can't go on. . . . I knew it weeks ago, but I wouldn't give him up without a battle. I mapped out a gay campaign. I fought for him night after night, pretending I didn't know. I did my best, even when I was blind sick. . . . I thought I was getting back in his heart—and I was just getting in his hair. . . ."

"You go to bed," Mrs. Marsan urged. She was alarmed at Vivien's attitude and appearance. "You're all done in."

Vivien got up unsteadily. Mrs. Marsan helped her to the bedroom. It seemed strangely drear for all its satin furbishings.

Wearily Vivien took off the housecoat. "It's so heavy . . ." she complained. Her girdle left welts where it had tortured her waist to slimness. She got into drab flannelette pajamas found hidden under her lingerie—"I wore them when I was in the hospital and they're so easy on my aches—" and crawled gratefully into bed.

"You can write him when you feel better," Mrs. Marsan comforted. "Maybe it's just a mood he'll get over."

"No." On the bedside table where, secret in the back of the drawer, Vivien kept the calendar record of her dosing, she noticed the tray with the stubs of cigarettes Burt smoked during the sleepless night before. She turned her head aside. "I won't write this time. No—echoes."

"Well," Mrs. Marsan recalled something from her scrapbook, "they say it's the unusual woman who goes out of a man's life without slamming the door."

"When you leave, pick up that box on the kitchen table."

Vivien's closed eyes were deeply circled. "It's a pie I was bringing home for Burt."

"Can't I fix you something? Glass of hot milk maybe?"

Vivien gagged.

"Oh, God, no. Just leave the light on in the bathroom."

She lay there in loose and almost voluptuous relaxation. Life was not altogether callous; even when cruel, it had its compensations. Now at last she could afford the luxury of being sick.

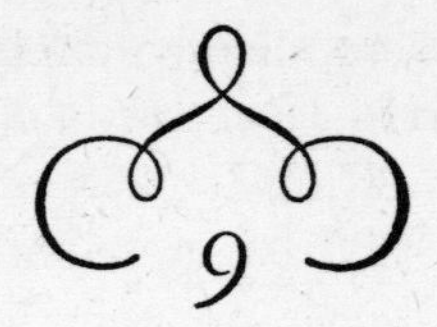

THE WINDOW was up and the sixth of March streamed into the room bright and balmy. Joey was putting bread crumbs out on the sill for the birds.

"March come in nice she go out nasty." Pearl always swabbed her face with witchhazel after dusting. "That what it say in the Bible."

"Pearl hasn't known what she's talking about since yesterday," Joey said.

"I hear the minister read you out the Bible about the lion and the lamb past Thursday, don't I?"

"It was the *wolf* and the lamb," Joey amended.

"Wasn't it the sheep and the goats?" Mrs. Marsan struggled to remember and found it tiring. "I didn't bring the opera glasses, Joey. Sig's taken them to Sobel. I brought *Tess*. I thought we could pass some of the morning reading."

"It's only the first week—" Joey turned around in alarm. "Didn't you get your check from The Plantation?"

"Oh, sure. But I had to pay Doc forty-seven dollars and twenty cents out of it. No—he knocked off the twenty cents," she corrected, "because I've been buying a lot of medicine lately."

"That a expensive honeymoon that dog had." Pearl looked at Lady, formless as a spreading cloud.

"He said I could pay it any time, as long as I added the interest. But that day I went to get my nitro prescription filled, all of a sudden he says I have to pay it right away. He kept reminding me so hard I gave it to him the minute I got my check."

"But you still ought to have a balance without going to Sobel."

"Sig wanted to borrow fifty dollars. That was the only way I could lend it to him without putting a hole in the money I have left to run the house. Sig's got a sure thing." Her eyes sparked. "Blonde Blitz. Three year old in the one and an eighth mile seventh. Sig's been studying up on her and she can't miss. He even got the weather reports wired from Coral Gables to be sure the track'd be right. It's part of the system he figured out. I gave him an extra five to place for me. She'll pay ten for one."

"*He* pay five hundred for nothing, that last race to jail," Pearl said.

"That horse has *got* to win." Mrs. Marsan tried to cross her short fat fingers. "If she don't we'll all be in the street. Doc says if the bank don't loosen up by the fifteenth he'll buy at their price and get the difference back cutting the building into two-room apartments to draw more rent."

"What houses got to do with horses?" Pearl inquired.

"I know Sig wants to beat him to buying it," Joey said. "He was asking Edna if she wanted to participate in co-operative purchase, or something."

"That's an idea he got from Mr. Cernak, but he's improved it. Mr. Cernak thought everybody who could should put in a percentage to make up the ten thousand deposit and share the responsibility, and he said *he'd* keep the books on it. But Sig thinks it would be simpler just for himself to buy the building with borrowed money. So Hannah's putting up her three thousand and Uncle Benny his five, and Mr. Brinkmann's lending a thousand and Elvira five hundred. But Sig needs five hundred more and he's got to get it out of Blonde Blitz. Or the fifteenth will be here and we won't—soon enough, anyway."

"Win or lose, *I* won't be here," Pearl said.

"Did Edna—" Mrs. Marsan knew Edna was furious with Pearl for having told her nothing about Phil Cassidy.

"Two weeks ago Miss Edna want to fire me." Pearl grinned. "Now she just as mad because I give notice to quit."

"You quitting?"

"Something terrible happen to me," Pearl said importantly.

"It's Bernie," Joey explained. "He didn't proposition her."

"Trouble with you, you've got no patience, Pearl."

"He *proposed,*" Joey said.

"I rather be took up than hook up, but since that the only way to get him, I got to marry him."

"Well!" Mrs. Marsan drew a long breath. "That shows how amorous he was, all along."

"Might be amorous," Pearl protested, "but it not *glamorous.*"

"Worse things could happen than having a foot to your bed, Pearl," Mrs. Marsan said.

"Got no foot," Pearl smiled. "Miss Vivien give me hers and her satin spread and pillows and everything. I can have all the symptoms without the disease. That happen sometimes."

"And she gave you all those wonderful negligées and face creams and perfumes," Joey added.

"Is Vivien clearing out?" *No echoes.* I'm not surprised. . . .

"She going to live with Marie Louise till she get better, and Mr. Burt gone to Detroit to get a job with his brother." Pearl shrugged. "That what she say. . . ."

Mrs. Marsan wanted to know when Pearl was leaving.

"Well, it take longer getting ready for keeps than for kept. But Miss Edna knock my head off I don't give a week's notice, her stirring up a trip and all."

Mrs. Marsan turned to Joey. "You're really going?"

"Mexico," Joey said, without joy.

"When?"

"By plane. The twenty-third."

"Miss Edna try to get reservations sooner and can't. She in a devil of a hurry."

Joey filled up. Mrs. Marsan opened the book quickly. She was glad they were at an exciting place. A large dog-ear marked the page where the book fell open, coffee-stained and pencil-marked like a dirty face.

"Alec, the father of her dead child, finds Tess again after Angel, learning the truth, left her on their wedding night," Mrs. Marsan summed up. "You remember?"

"Angel in Brazil. Everybody around here going away, even in stories."

"That's right." Mrs. Marsan cleared her throat. " 'His voice sank, and a hot archness shot from his own black eyes. "You temptress, Tess; you dear damned witch of Babylon—I could not resist you as soon as I met you again!" ' " She read the passage where Alec reviles his absent rival and makes renewed advances to Tess, giving it all the emotion of which she was capable in an effort to win Joey's interest. " ' "I am without defense, Alec! A good man's honour is in my keeping—think—be ashamed!" ' "

There were a couple of good things in this chapter, she thought as she read on, which ordinarily Joey would have wanted her to mark off. In the absence of Joey's request, she did it herself. But it was no use reading further. Pearl was polishing her fingernails with a dreamy air, and Joey, looking out the window, was listening to her own thoughts. Only Lady was really in the room. Mrs. Marsan glanced up at the sound of mad scratching. Lady was clawing away at the rug. Before long she would have dug a hole through it.

2

It was five days before the fifty-nine were up, but Lady's burden was so large she seemed unable to bear it longer. She could hardly walk, the fringe of her ready teats almost touching the floor under the weight above them. She was unusually big, fantastic. Mrs. Marsan blamed herself for being unprepared with rubber sheeting, for she intended that Lady should be confined in her own bed. Joey gave her the oilcloth off the kitchen table.

Coming out of Joey's, she observed that the door of Coral Sands' apartment was open. She looked in and saw Coral's leopard skin coat thrown over the back of a chair. Lady barked, one stuffy yelp, at the sound of high-heeled steps in the rooms beyond. Coral appeared with a pile of towels in her arms.

"Hello. Come on in," she said.

She looked fine today. Her eyes were sunny and the lush fruitiness was back in her lips and the curve of her cheek.

"You look better." Mrs. Marsan went over her. A trifle fuller, too—much prettier than that snapbean style.

"I certainly feel better." Coral lounged into a chair and crossed her picture-perfect legs. She reached to the table beside her for a cigarette box; then reconsidering, pushed it away.

Mrs. Marsan was drawn irresistibly to the leopard skin.

"No mystery, Marsie. I bought it back, that's all— Hard to break old habits, you know."

"You're back here to stay?"

"No. I'm back here to *go*. Just getting a few things. I have a date with a second-hand dealer to make me a price on my furnishings. I notified the bank I'll be out by the fifteenth."

Coral looked around the well-dressed room and drumming

her fingers on the chair arm began to hum happily. Everything about her indicated a feeling of freedom and relief.

"Where're you going?"

"Doubling up with my girl friend in the Village. We got a garret. It's grand."

Girl friend. . . . Mrs. Marsan matched the idea with the return of the coat and Coral's release from worry and the pieces did not fit.

"You see that writing desk over there?" Coral pointed to an ornate piece of furniture in the corner under the lamp. "I'm not selling that because I've had this guy look at it before and he won't give me what it might be worth. It's supposed to be a Louis XV escritoire."

"It's nice." Mrs. Marsan appraised it. "But it's got a leg broke."

"That's what makes it valuable. Antiques are no good if they're new. Some drip I used to go with was a collector." Coral smiled ruefully. "He collected everything but the check. I dropped him. Anyway, he gave me that."

"What's it worth?"

"I don't know. I've had a couple of art dealers look at it—times I was in a jam—and they said it was a fake. Wouldn't give me five dollars for it. I'd take five hundred."

"Adrian Larsch would know, I bet. But I don't believe she'd buy it. She's investing in travel."

"Well, I thought I'd have it lugged over to your place instead of punishing it with a jolt down to the Village and up to the garret, and if I send anybody over to look at it, you can show it off."

"Sure," Mrs. Marsan agreed. "Maybe I'll hear of somebody who's interested myself."

Coral laughed. "The way *you* hear things, Marsie, maybe you will. I'd better give you my address so you can let me know if you get a nibble." She went to the escritoire and scratched out a line. "Writing a garret address at a royal desk is the height of something—I don't know what."

Coral handed her the slip of paper and sat down again in the big chair. Her suit was getting shoddy, but she looked exceptionally well. There were things Mrs. Marsan was dying to know. . . .

"It's nice you can keep your coat," she hinted, her eyes hitting the target again.

"Sometimes I think it's made of rubber, the way it snaps back." Coral tucked her legs up under her in the chair. "Of course, I'm keeping my baby, too."

Mrs. Marsan jerked forward as if someone had pushed her. "You didn't do what you wanted?"

"I wanted the baby. After the panic died down, I knew that's what I wanted. If I can't keep Burt, I want to keep his baby."

"Now you're talking sense." The paralyzing shock of Coral's first announcement lifted. Her heart began to bat back and forth like a punching bag.

"I'm not so sure. But when you're in love you're not supposed to be sensible. It's funny—like a dry drunk. I love Burt —enough for anything."

"Does he know what's happened?"

Coral shook her head.

"When I told him good-by, I didn't know myself." She sat up straight. "Listen, Marsie. I'm not one to turn on the hose and the heroics. Bad fish smells better to me than one of these tearful acts where the woman gives up the man she loves for some noble motive. But what Nick Dinapolis said that day about women wanting what don't belong to them and men following fluff struck hard. I wasn't breaking my neck to break Vivien's heart. Burt felt like a man with me and an inferiority complex with her, but she saw him first. She didn't love Burt any more than I did, but she'd loved him longer. It was only decent to give her back what was hers. If they were married, I might have felt different—I don't know. To me, lovers are more hands-off than husbands. A husband's got to leave something by law, but a lover just leaves a hole. . . . It was hard to break with Burt and I kept putting it off. But when I flipped that nickel, I did what it told me. I made Burt believe I was through. I told him there was somebody else. I—" Coral broke off. She laughed quietly. "Did I ever think I'd be in soap opera—highly scented. . . ."

The bell rang, and she ran to the kitchen to buzz the caller up. "That's the second-hand dealer—"

She came back for a final word.

"I'm taking a new job, Marsie. One where you don't have to stand or wear a rig that shows your waistline. You sit down in a smock, packing biscuits. If you're a good girl and keep your mouth shut, I'll send you something to open it for. A nice box of biscuits."

As Mrs. Marsan stepped into the hall, Lady dragging at her heels, she had a feeling, from the careful click of the latch, that someone had just entered the next apartment. Coral's door had been open. She wondered how much Vivien heard. . . .

3

Mrs. Marsan's letter to Burt was finished. It had taken her several hours and her last sheet of paper to write. The pyramid of torn scraps piled up beside the dictionary borrowed from Joey Brent proved what an ordeal composition had been. It was particularly hard to let Burt know, in a genteel way, that Coral was pregnant. She had pondered the phrasing until she was exhausted, compromising at last on repeated references to Coral's delicate condition. That sounded nice, she thought, and if Burt was too male to get it the first time, he would at least get suspicious the sixth.

She checked Coral's address to be sure she had copied it correctly, and now she had only to tackle the matter of remembering Burt's. Her tired mind reconstructed the Sunday afternoon in Vivien's apartment. "Just remember pen—then look in the phone book." She closed her eyes. A pen stuck in the phone book was the picture she had memorized, but nothing came of it. *Getting old. . . . My head's not as good as it used to be. . . .* But you wouldn't look for Pen in the phone book; you'd look for Villars.

Villars, and Pen, too. . . .

She had it. She took her letter and hastened down to the drugstore. Doc resurrected a Detroit directory from under the counter and blew off the dust. There it was. *Villars, Russell, Mftrs Agt. Penobscot Bldg.* Doc lent his fountain pen grudgingly, injured because he had taken time and trouble to fish out the book for a nonprofit three-cent stamp instead of a long-distance call.

She was lucky to meet Adrian on the stairs. Adrian resisted at first with frozen reserve, but thawed at mention of Louis XV. She made it clear, however, that she had only a minute because this evening she was going to a Greek drama and she had to get dinner and dress.

It took Adrian less than a minute to decide that the escritoire was definitely spurious. The workmanship, she diagnosed, was a tremendously clever imitation, but the materials were wrong and the finish was positively only modern vulgar varnish toned down, a common knavish trick. Having delivered her estimate somewhat indignantly, she dashed out only to become snagged in Mr. Ingalls' surprised but grateful arms.

"I beg your pardon," she said regally.

"All my fault." Mr. Ingalls' face lit up like a lamp, with pleasure.

Mrs. Marsan closed her door with an obvious noise, and applied her good ear to the panel.

"Did you get my note?" Mr. Ingalls asked.

"Yes. Thank you very much, but I have no books to return to the library."

"I suppose you're too busy to draw any. . . ." He rallied quickly: "But I'd be glad to get whatever you wanted, any time!"

"I don't want anything."

Mr. Ingalls faced the impasse speechlessly.

"Please excuse me." Adrian was glacial. "I'm going to see *Antigone* tonight."

"I like Sophocles, too!" Mrs. Marsan had a picture of him barring Adrian's door, desperately trying to keep her a moment longer. "Just a minute, Miss Larsch. Why can't we do some of these things together?"

"Why should we?"

"Because—because—" Poor fellow, he was stammering. "Well, because I think we have something to offer each other. We like the same things—"

"Do we?"

"What I mean is—I can't explain it exactly. I suppose I'm afflicted with what DeQuincey calls the 'burden of the incommunicable.' But I thought—" He broke on an embarrassed laugh. "I thought we could be friends," he finished painfully.

"You seem to be well supplied with friends already. I'm afraid I could never compete with their tastes or accomplishments."

"What?" Mr. Ingalls sounded baffled.

"Besides the opium eater you've just quoted, communists, inebriates, and strump—" Adrian caught herself "—that impossible Mrs. Marsan."

"What's the matter with Mrs. Marsan?" Hurt surprise. That nice Mr. Ingalls. . . .

"I knew from the minute I examined that china. It's not Haviland, Limoges. It's Steubenville, Ohio."

"China." You could hear Mr. Ingalls frowning.

"She claims to be the mistress of a plantation manor." Adrian's laugh was two tinkling notes. "She's only the mistress of a cheap plaid shirt."

Plaid shirt. . . .

"I don't follow—"

"*I* had to follow it down the steps one morning."

Bill!—Well. Nothing so vicious as a virtuous woman. . . .

"If *she's* a southern aristocrat, I'm queen of the Eskimos." The words fell like hail, cold and stinging.

A rumbling silence followed, like the gathering of a storm. Mrs. Marsan had seen Mr. Ingalls angry once before, the night Ruthie reported the raid, and had learned that the wrath of a quiet man was awesome. Now she could feel the lightning flashes through the door.

"That's just what you are." Mr. Ingalls spoke with low thunder. "A frozen, unfeeling, self-appointed throne sitter." His tongue was loosened at last, and eloquence broke from it like a cloudburst. "With all you know, you don't know what an aristocrat is. Nor a communist. Nor an inebriate, either. With all your learning, you overlooked Solomon. With all your getting, you forgot to get *understanding!*" His voice had risen and he reefed it in with scorn. "I thought you had everything—*everything*. But you haven't got the only thing that *counts!*"

Mrs. Marsan held her breath, her eyes bulging. She waited for Adrian's answer. Instead, a door slammed, with such violence that windows rattled.

She turned the knob and peeked through a thread of a crack. It must have been Mr. Ingalls' door because he was gone. And Adrian stood there still, a statue of consternation.

Mr. Ingalls had done that to Adrian— Mrs. Marsan could not believe her senses. The uneasy feeling assailed her again that Mr. Ingalls was going out of his head. . . .

But she was disturbed only for a moment. For out of the words exchanged in the hall, one fluttered about her like a shimmering moth. It was the word mistress. Adrian thought— She went and smiled at herself in the mirror. Who said she was getting old? She never felt younger or looked better in her life.

4

By nine o'clock the sky was a dripping sponge and the dismal tick of slow rain mingled with Lady's whimpering. She lay in the middle of Mrs. Marsan's bed, in a nest of soft rag over Joey's oilcloth. Absorbent cotton and a sterilized manicure scissors loaned by Elvira waited on the dresser. Mrs. Marsan sat by the window, drinking hot coffee. Her hand trembled.

She went reluctantly to answer a knock on the door. Ruthie stood there with Max balanced on her bony little hip.

"Papa says to tell you she made it in real style," Ruthie quoted accurately.

A low quivering cry came from the bedroom. Mrs. Marsan turned with a jerk. She was conscious of the cool dampness of sweat on her face. Ruthie extended her turtle neck beyond the doorway.

"Can I come in?"

"No," Mrs. Marsan said. "No, not now. I'm busy."

Ruthie loitered, hoping she might relent.

"Papa would have come himself, but his stomach's upset."

"Oh, that's all right."

"No, it's not!" Ruthie adhered to facts. "He threw up all his supper and he's got to lay down."

"He'll be better in the morning," Mrs. Marsan said. "You run along now."

She edged Ruthie out and locked the door quietly. She could hear her strutting down the hall in a huff.

When she returned to the bedroom it was happening. Lady's eyes followed her, mournful and dark with uncomprehended misery. She wanted to say something to Lady, but the words hardened to rock in her throat. She went to the bathroom for no reason and when she came back the first baby was there.

All the tremble left her hands. The scissors were firm in her soft fat fingers as she snipped the navel cord. Gently she swabbed the slime from the raw spot. She dipped the scissors in the antiseptic solution she had bought from Doc and dried them in cotton. She waited. This was the second. . . .

She could not have said how long she stood there, bending over the bed, performing over and over her simple act of surgery. Her face was as wet as if she had held it to the rain, and her eyelashes were beaded. She wiped her eyes on the back of her kimono sleeve, rolled up. Then she waited a long time, leaning against the wall.

Now that it was finished her hands and knees went to water. She was as tired as Lady, lying there like a limp empty sack. Automatically she began to count . . . one, two, three. . . . She wiped her eyes once more, though they were dry and gaping clear, and started to count again. Four, five, six. . . . She could hardly believe it. Seven, eight, nine. . . .

Eleven. . . . Eleven soft lumps like unbaked biscuits.

"You've made it, Lady," she said, panting. "You've made it in real style."

The words had a familiar ring. *Papa says to tell you.* . . . A rocket went up in her head, bursting to a brilliance of realization.

Blonde Blitz had won.

Shaking, she reached for her sweater hanging over the back of a near-by chair, and drew the small brown bottle from the pocket. She had time only to unscrew the cap and slip a tablet under her tongue before the cramp coiled tight in her chest. She let herself down on the upper edge of the bed, reclining against the headpiece, her arm flung out loosely beside the new puppies.

The rain had quickened and was plashing gaily against the windowpanes. Lady stirred and started to lick her hand.

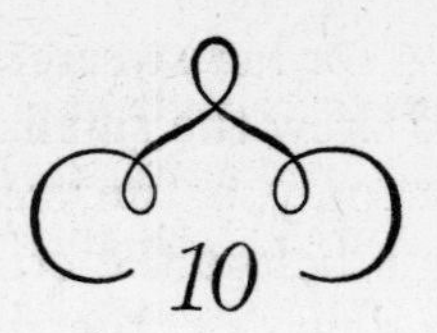

10

WITH the sun still in Pisces," the Daily Horoscope read, "an active program is slated by the stars for the Ides of March. Throughout the ages the fifteenth has been feared as a day of disaster, so try to avoid running risks. On the other hand, if danger can be averted, this date is not without its rewards in pleasant surprises."

Mrs. Marsan went over it several times, without being able to decide whether the outlook was good or bad. In any case, she was resolved not to touch her dwindling cash in another attempt to secure a smile from Fortune, whose laugh, paying her fifty dollars for her five at Tropical Park, was loud but short. Sig's perfect system—by which, if she put the whole fifty on a gelding called Happy Harry in the Oaklawn handicap, she could triple her money—had failed sensationally.

The Watchword for today was no less equivocal and Mrs. Marsan sat meditating a long time, wondering if it was worth a place in her scrapbook. It was Charles Frohman's last words: "Why fear death? It is the most beautiful adventure in life. . . ." She knew that some people feared living as much as dying, and they missed a great deal of fun. So perhaps Charles Frohman was right. Death was something happening, not something ceasing to happen, as almost everybody believed.

Carefully she considered the subject of adventure. Can people who stay in one spot all the time be adventurous? The idea shaped nebulously, without words, that adventure could be a state of mind as well as a state of activity. Her one adventurous act was in coming to New York after Henry died; she had always longed for the excitement of a great city. Perhaps she felt that way on account of having once loved Louis. Or perhaps on account of having married Henry. . . .

In the end she concluded with a lift of pleasure and some surprise that she was among those who liked and sought adventure. A warm thrill climbed up her spine. She seized the scissors and clipped out the paragraph with a sort of pride.

Her scrapbook was full to the last inch now and there was no place to paste this latest entry. Unless she used the very first page, which was bare back and front except for her favorite Watchword, enshrined in the exact middle. She hated to desecrate the hallowed spot with an addition. When she opened the book she liked to see this bit of newsprint shining there alone, like the evening star in the sky. "I expect to pass through this world—" She had started to read it for the thousandth time when Vivien knocked.

The large cornflakes box containing Lady and her puppies was in a snug corner of the living room, by the radiator. Mr. Ingalls had cut down one side to within a few inches of the floor, so that Lady could step out or look over while the puppies remained safely confined. Vivien stood for a long time watching them. Their confused ancestry had compromised rather startlingly on silky ears and a wavy coat covered with Dalmatian spots. All save one boy, who reversed the entire order by being black and curly as lamb, with three white dots. He was for Joey—her choice—and she had named him Domino.

Mrs. Marsan told Vivien how Lady had been photographed with her family the day before.

"I had Nick Dinapolis over to see them. His eyes nearly fell out. He says the longer he lives the more women surprise him, furred by nature or furred by man. He had to hurry back to the tavern and take a good stiff drink. Then he got to thinking he ought to celebrate, on account of the father being his Mildew, and these two reporters happened to be there, because they were in the neighborhood interviewing somebody. So he invited them to drink with him and they were so interested when he told them why he was celebrating, they came right over to get the whole story and a flashlight picture for the Sunday paper."

"They're sweet," Vivien said pensively.

She stooped and stroked Lady's head, then picked up a puppy from the groping, greedy tangle and held it close, combing its soft hair with her fingertips. Its legs hung over the side of her hand and its funny little belly sprawled like a frog's. She looked at its newly opened wash-blue eyes and pink nose and smiled.

"Look out," Mrs. Marsan warned. "Company's got a way of going to their kidneys."

Vivien returned the puppy gently to Lady and stood up. Mrs. Marsan observed that she looked rested. She had on the comfortable blue suit she called a country casual, and it gave her an easy, natural air instead of that strung-up and struggling slimness.

"I came to say good-by, and to ask you a favor."

"I'm sorry to see you go," Mrs. Marsan said sincerely. "Anything I can do—"

Vivien brought a padded envelope out of her pocket.

"You might think this funny, and you may not want to do it. But I'd like you to give this money to Coral Sands."

"I don't mind." Mrs. Marsan was trying to understand. "What do you want me to say to her?"

"That's just it. I want *you* to think of something to say to her. I don't want her to know it came from me."

"Is it much?" The envelope looked fat.

"Five hundred dollars. I sold the earrings to Sobel. I didn't want them any more."

The information staggered Mrs. Marsan.

"I don't want you to think I'm trying to do anything grand," Vivien said matter-of-factly. "I'm not doing this for Coral Sands. I'm doing it for myself. Do you think you can make up a story and get her to take it?"

Mrs. Marsan's eye traveled to the hypocritical Louis XV escritoire.

"I won't have any trouble about that."

"Thank you." Vivien handed her the envelope. "I know Burt will go to her and I want them to have something to start on. I can't bear to think of Burt hard up." She laughed nervously. "I know what you're thinking. But love is never foolish—while it's always selfish. I want my own peace of mind about him, because—I still love Burt."

Mrs. Marsan strove to word what she thought.

"Well, when you can love like that, I guess you've got something even if you've lost it," she said.

She shook hands with Vivien at the door.

2

Jean worked from one to six. There was time to get a sheet of paper and an envelope from her before she left.

Several knocks failed to rouse her. It certainly was funny. . . . Maybe Jean was gone already, though Mrs. Marsan always heard her step passing in the hall. Or maybe she was just too taken up with Vivien and missed it.

Or maybe. . . .

Growing apprehension spread to the roots of Mrs. Marsan's hair. She had been uneasy again about Jean. For a while there, everything was wonderful; Jean bloomed and was even buoyant. Mrs. Marsan thought—and feared—the shining eyes reflected Eric Arnold. When she saw his punctual letters in

Jean's box latterly she felt somehow vexed; perhaps it was because they were always so disappointing. The nearest he had ever come to being human was the time he alluded to the "charming personality" that spoke from Jean's correspondence. Yet she knew Jean waited for these gems of disgusting propriety as if they were the world's most exciting reading. Then, suddenly, the letters stopped. It must be nearly three weeks since Jean had had a word. At first Mrs. Marsan felt guilty because she was glad. She hoped Eric had really quit writing. But she had been a fool not to figure on Jean's reaction. Jean chuted into a state of depression that was almost as bad as the beginning. Now Mrs. Marsan was more anxious for her because Eric didn't write than she had been because he did.

The terrible things she read in the paper stampeded her mind and in a frenzy she beat on the door with both fists.

Jean opened at last. She was in the flannel robe, her face masked with the dead uninterest familiar to Mrs. Marsan from the first days of their acquaintance.

"Are you sick?" Mrs. Marsan pushed her way in.

Jean said "No" and nothing else.

Mrs. Marsan felt flattened. It would be a job to make talk. She was too upset at the discouraging turn in the situation to try.

"I came to borrow a sheet of paper and an envelope."

Jean went to a box on the table and brought out a sheaf of stationery. It was very good paper, her initials embossed with quiet taste in the corner. *For Eric,* Mrs. Marsan thought, with a twinge of resentment toward him. Why couldn't Jean have been writing gay things on gay paper, to somebody who could forget his manners once in a while and just be a man? . . .

"I only want one sheet," she said, taking a leaf.

"No." Jean choked. "Take it. Take it all. Please."

"I don't need all that." Mrs. Marsan held out the paper. "And you will."

"No. No, I won't," Jean said. "Not any more."

Her face of a sudden became absurdly childish. Her lip trembled and for a moment she struggled with tears. She kept her head averted as if it pained her to look at the paper. Mrs. Marsan laid the surplus down on the table.

"You'd better be getting off to work."

"I'm not going today," Jean said. "I—don't feel up to it."

This unexpected set-back—just when Jean was getting on so well. . . . With a pang Mrs. Marsan recognized the old problem of getting the girl away from herself. Now she would have to start all over again. Maybe Phil Cassidy had a friend—young, nice-looking, steady—the right kind of boy for Jean. She'd have to think about it before she asked him—not too fast. She had jumped too fast, and far, in the case of Eric Arnold. But one thing at a time. She must get this letter off to Coral first.

She left Jean until later and came back to her own rooms, putting out the pen and ink which seemed now to have played the part of wolf in sheep's clothing. Laying aside for the present Jean's relapse, she bent all her forces to writing Coral. Since she had insisted one sheet of paper would be enough, she was careful to make a clean job of her letter the first time. It was a good thing she still had Joey Brent's dictionary because she had to look up escritoire, marveling at the crazy spelling which had nothing to do with the way it sounded. She wrote it "Louie" XV, and paused to look at the name with old-time tenderness running through her head like a tune. The person who bought the escritoire, she told Coral, was—she had seen the phrase somewhere, and liked it—"a lady of distinction."

Doc would be eating his lunch now, so she would have to wait to get the money order to enclose. Meantime it might be a good idea to bring back Joey's dictionary while she thought of it. She hoped she would have to write no more letters; they hashed her brains. Yet she had written two lately, and never two without three. . . .

Thinking Joey was alone, since Pearl had finished out her week's notice day before yesterday, she brought Domino for company. But Phil was there. They were eating lunch in the living room, a grave lunch such as people have at funeral homes.

"I took a taxi out and I'll take one back. I've only an hour and a half from my desk," Phil explained.

Nobody said a word for minutes. Mrs. Marsan could feel a current of desperate calculation rushing into the vacuum. One week before the departure for Mexico. Not even the last Wednesday afternoon, because Edna was coming home around two every day now. Seven more days, and seven more hours snatched from the middle of each of them. No—six, because a Sunday, with Edna home, came in between.

Joey shook off the spell and held out her hands for Domino. Her plate was barely touched; neither she nor Phil were displaying eager appetites.

"How can even God make anything so lovely?" She held Domino's black silkiness to her cheek.

"Don't do that before Edna," Mrs. Marsan cautioned. "You know how she is about germs."

Phil put down his fork and his hand tightened to a fist on the table.

"Nothing could be more deadly than Edna's attitude!" he said angrily.

"Phil. . . ." Joey laid Domino in her lap. She reached over and covered his fist with her hand.

"Edna gives me a pain," Mrs. Marsan confided, "even without germs."

Joey was troubled. "She says her whole life is wrapped up in me."

"That's what makes it wrong for both of you," Phil stated. "What counts in any kind of love is not how *much* but *how*. I don't mind other people being literally loved to death but I can't see it happening to you."

"I always thought it would be more comfortable to have an octopus love you than Edna," Mrs. Marsan said.

"Everything she does, it's because she thinks it's for my good." Joey looked miserable. "But I don't want to be what Edna wants to make me. I want to be myself!"

"Maybe being yourself," Mrs. Marsan suggested, "you'd be doing something for *Edna's* good."

Phil's hand was still a fist under Joey's.

"Edna has got to face reality. She's got to get out of her phantom world of false values and sentimental fallacies. I'm the last one to object to sentiment when it's healthy, but when one sister gets a grip on the other one like Edna has on you, it's something for a psychiatrist." His face gloomed over. "That's why I can't fight her. I could fight Japs on Okinawa because they were real, but I can't get at those goblins in Edna's head."

"She's got the tickets," Joey said hopelessly.

"I know what I'd do." Mrs. Marsan was looking around for a weapon with which Phil could fight Edna, and found it.

He looked at her with interest.

"I'd get the license," she said.

Phil's fist melted and his fingers went around Joey's.

"Shall I?" he asked. "We can go together, in Brenda's car."

Joey shook her head yes. The larkspur blue of her eyes was deep and glad.

Then Edna stood there, as acutely felt by the three of them as if she were in the flesh. And Joey's thought, a little frightened, could be read as clearly as if it were written on the wall. *But we may never use it. . . .*

3

Doc Kincaid looked sick. He had the limp, greenish appearance of seaweed. Mrs. Marsan had never known him as needing to call on his own stock for a cure. Now he had just opened a pack of the peppermint tablets Sig always took and clapped one into his mouth.

"You not feeling right?" The answer was there. What she wanted to know was why.

"I've got indigestion," Doc said sourly. He changed the subject to one more pleasing to him. "What do you want?"

"My prescription refilled." She was saving the best bite for last. "I brought the bottle"—she dipped into her sweater pocket for it—"so you could get the number."

Doc looked at the date on the label. "It ran out quick," he observed, glancing at her sideways. He coughed and added, "Ten to fifteen minutes to have it ready."

"I'll walk Lady around and pick it up on my way back."

Doc leaned over and scowled at Lady. "You'll go broke feeding eleven kiyoodles," he predicted.

"Don't lose any sleep about me going broke." Mrs. Marsan chewed the best bite with relish, producing the envelope containing Vivien's money. The pack of bills was as thick as a deck of cards. "Give me a money order for five hundred dollars, payable to Coral Sands."

Doc stared. A nerve began to twitch in his thin jaw.

"I'll have to give you five for a hundred each." He sounded weak.

"That makes it."

Doc counted the pile three times. Then he went in the back to put it in his safe. He came out again and wrote up the money orders, his lips tight.

Mrs. Marsan enclosed the orders and sealed the envelope. "Let me have a stamp."

"That's twenty-two cents each, a dollar ten, and three fifty for the medicine, and three for the stamp." Doc's head was such an adding machine that she expected a paper ribbon with figures on it to pop out of his mouth. "Four sixty-three."

Mrs. Marsan handed him her last five-dollar bill. She would have to run credit at Brinkmann's again.

"I have a sale on talcum, thirty-seven cents with the tax." Doc put her change down on the counter.

"I can't use that cheap stuff." She scooped it up. "It gives me rash. I've been getting my special blend on Fifth Avenue."

"That system's working . . ." Doc said sadly.

"Sig owes it all to you." Mrs. Marsan shoved the specter of Happy Harry aside. "He had lots of time at the station house to work on it."

"A fine way he's showing his appreciation—giving me six months to clear out!"

He's changed from green to red like a traffic light, Mrs. Marsan thought.

"He corners enough on that system to buy the building, and then he tells me this morning his brother-in-law wants this place for a kosher shop!"

Mrs. Marsan tugged at Lady to get up. At the door she turned and asked, "What was the name of that Australian weapon you were telling me about?"

"What?" Doc Kincaid's face was a go sign again. "The boomerang."

"It sure is restless," Mrs. Marsan said.

She left him to his indigestion tablets.

Loud confusion shook the tavern as she approached. Above the fracas of crashing glass and shouting rose Jessamine's voice, full and furious. Mrs. Marsan hurried nightmarishly, the weight in her chest holding her back. When at last she reached there, Nick Dinapolis, shooting out of the entrance in blind flight, nearly knocked her down.

The few customers still in the tavern huddled in their booths, looking out at Jessamine in fascination and fear. She swept before the rail in great dramatic strides, the structure of her heavy hair tottering, the green veil around her throat loose and flying. One after the other she picked up the glass steins Nick kept at the end of the counter and raging to the center, hurled them right and left, her large sleeves falling back from her powerful white arms. The steins struck the bottles lined up with the shine of jewels around the semicircular bar, shattering them to the floor like tenpins. The space before the huge mirror was a shambles of splintered glass.

"Smash the existing order!" Jessamine screamed. "Down with the Diamond Horseshoe!"

She rushed toward a bottle on the counter and swinging it above her head like a club, let it go with a force that shivered the mirror from top to bottom. The glass flew out as in an explosion.

"Jessamine! Stop it! *Stop!*" Mrs. Marsan put all her breath into her shriek.

Jessamine turned around, exulting. She looked like a mad giantess.

"Nitroglycerin! Did you bring it?" She held out her hand. "Give it to me! It cures everything! Inequality—capitalism—everything!"

Nick came in with Donegan and three other officers. Mrs. Marsan looked out and saw two gray squad cars in the street and a knot of people.

"Come along, Miss Cernak," Donegan said.

Jessamine was bewildered. Blood ran down her cheek where a piece of glass had hit her.

"Everything will be all right. My brother says so. This is the sign." She held up her hands with the thumbs tucked under. "Four four. Then everybody can go to the opera."

"You're going to the opera right now," one of the officers said.

Jessamine went with them docilely, joyous.

4

The fight with Edna left her as shaken as if they had used their fists instead of their tongues. Oddly, she must have dozed off, waiting for the tablet to dissolve and the spasm to go. Her left side felt numb from shoulder to fingertips. She tried to clench her hand and found it stiff. It probably came from having been cramped against the end of the sofa.

She glanced over at the clock on the table. It was five-thirty, more than two hours since Edna swooped down on her as she dragged herself upstairs after the trouble at the tavern. She heard Edna again, the greeting zinging at her from the top of the steps like a poisoned arrow. *I've been waiting for you. . . .*

It was all true, because there was Domino back, a ball of slumber on the newspaper which Edna had used to convey him, at the other end of the sofa. *I told you distinctly I don't want her to have a dog. They carry germs.* Edna had a bug complex. She told Edna so. And what was that Edna said. . . . *You have a keyhole complex. And I'll thank you to keep your eye away from mine.*

It was all right to be antiseptic, but you didn't have to be anti everything. Maybe it was natural for Edna to fear microbes, when she'd seen polio carry off one sister and cripple the next; but fear could be stretched so far it didn't make sense. You're a jugful of germs yourself, she flung at Edna. And Edna flung back that at least she kept her virus out of other people's lives.

She gave it to Edna good, but she had to admit Edna gave it to her better. Edna had lightning on her lip and it knew where to strike. *If you must pick men up out of the street, pick them for yourself!* Edna was jealous—green, shaking jealous. Jealous of me too—that's it. Jealous of Joey's every little dream and every little joy that wasn't Edna-inspired. Putting down borax and sugar for Joey's natural instincts, stamping them out the way she stamped out pests. Joey had to belong to Edna, because Edna found a fine, selfish martyrdom in belonging to Joey. She told Edna as much. *Your opinion is worth as little to me as other people's privacy is worth to you,* Edna lashed at her.

Before it was all over their words were ringing like hammer blows on anvils. *Stay out! Out of our home and out of our business, that's all I ask you!* You ought to practice what you preach. Stay out of your sister's business, that's what *I'm* asking *you. Whose sister is she? Yours or mine?* Yours, poor girl. *You couldn't even manage your own. I don't want your help, thank you.*

The noise must have got out and spread up the hall, because there was Joey standing in the doorway, her hands white at the knuckles where she gripped her props. "I don't want the dog. I don't want anything. Come on home, Edna," she said miserably.

Edna had to have the last white-hot word. *You see what your meddling's done, damn you . . . messing up her happiness as well as her health. . . .* Joey said, "I'm as healthy as a horse. It's you ruining *your* health and *your* happiness worrying about mine. . . ."

It was after they had gone that the iron hand started punching her from the inside, smashing her ribs. She no longer grabbed at her breast when it struck her, but at the sweater pocket where the brown bottle held relief. She could laugh now, thinking that she came out ahead of Edna after all. A delightful idea was winking at her . . . Edna said she would have the minister talk to her, and if that failed she would try the police. Let her send the minister. She'd be glad to have him—overjoyed—

She got on her feet with difficulty, a singing like steam in her head. Her left side was still asleep. With her right hand she picked Domino up off the newspaper, cradling him on her bosom. Poor mite. . . . He must be hungry. Domino woke up definitely on finding himself home at last, sliding over his sisters' and brothers' backs and stepping on necks and noses in his haste to get a belated lunch.

Returning to the sofa, she picked up the paper, which Edna had spread open in the middle. A large damp spot on one side testified to Domino's excitement during his adventure. It was an afternoon edition. She turned to the front page to see the headline, but her eyes never reached it. They stopped short on the picture of a young man whose face was as familiar as her own. The name ran together into a sooty blotch, then grew mirror clear.

John Ingalls.

She sank onto the sofa beside the paper, her eyes galloping along the lines faster than her mind could keep up with them . . . graduate of the University of Nebraska . . . the paper shortage, the book was written on the backs of obsolete A&P price lists . . . *Manuel Lisa* predicted to be easily the outstanding biographical novel of the decade . . . remarkable reality with which the author presents pioneer life at the stirring beginning of the last century . . . vigorous and eloquent prose, vividly peopled with unforgettable characters . . . Hollywood bidding. . . .

She could read no more. From habit she reached to her sweater pocket, though her heart was not hurting. It was just shouting hurrah.

Mr. Ingalls had built something. He had built it on paper, word on word. He had built—what did they say? There it was—a literary monument. He had built it with his brains instead of brawn and brick.

Later in the evening she saw Mr. Ingalls himself. Or *was*

it Mr. Ingalls—this distinguished man in white tie and tails with his hat in his gloved hand and a rich black overcoat thrown over his arm? She stood back to admire him. But for the way his forehead ruddied to the roots of his light brown hair as she exclaimed over him, and the steady gray eyes behind the glasses, he might have been somebody else.

He was on his way to a dinner at the Waldorf-Astoria, and came by to find out in detail what happened at the tavern. She told him all she knew.

"The people there said Nick refused to give her any more. I guess she was using up her credit too fast, and he wanted to save her from a long dry spell at the end of the month. He tries to ration it out to her. And usually she co-operates. But today she flew clean off the handle. She got an idea Nick was a criminal capitalist hoarding her share of goods."

"Miss Cernak is in the hospital," Mr. Ingalls said. "I had her sent to Bellevue."

"I'm waiting for her brother. He's not home yet."

"He won't be. He's held in bail."

Mrs. Marsan was astonished. "How'd they get *him?*"

"Donegan notified him about his sister. He rushed out there and staged a scene. You know how it is." Mr. Ingalls drew a resigned breath. "There's likely to be a little trouble because they have several counts against him already. That business with the boys last October, and this recent charge for unlawful assembly under the drugstore. Duffy didn't help by dramatizing the thing as The Underground and giving the judge some ridiculous secret sign. They'll find no fire, except Mr. Cernak's nuisance flame, but it may take time and talking to clear the smoke.

"Donegan's afraid they'll think the fire Jessamine started was arson, now. And the other witnesses had a lot to say about Jessamine yelling for nitroglycerin. But I explained it had nothing to do with dynamite."

"I'll see Donegan in the morning."

Mr. Ingalls had to go. A taxi was honking for him down in the street.

As she let him into the hall he came face to face with Adrian Larsch, standing before her apartment opposite. Mrs. Marsan could have sworn Adrian was waiting for him. She held the door open to see if she was right.

"I want to congratulate you." Adrian's smile was a work of art. "Edna Brent has told me the news. It's wonderful!"

At last—Adrian was going to be nice to Mr. Ingalls at last . . . Mrs. Marsan clutched the doorknob, holding her breath for his ecstatic reply.

"Thank you," said Mr. Ingalls, pounds of Adrian's former ice packing the words.

Mrs. Marsan's mouth fell open.

Adrian could not help feeling the chill. "The heady wine of success," she bantered. "Soon you won't be noticing your old friends."

"Those who really were my friends I'll keep," Mr. Ingalls said shortly.

"You've changed, already," she accused.

Mr. Ingalls gave her a long steady look.

"I've merely changed my mind, Miss Larsch, and that only about one thing. I myself haven't changed nor have I changed with respect to the kind of people I like. I still have my same cronies—with the possible exception of DeQuincey. You may remember confessing you could never compete with them."

The taxi downstairs complained. Mr. Ingalls excused himself to Adrian with a truly terrible politeness and wished her good night. There was a finality about his departure that seemed to leave a hole in the space where he had stood. Adrian, rooted there in the hall, was contemplating it with an annoyed frown.

Mrs. Marsan closed her door and leaned against it, suddenly weak with the realization of what Adrian had lost.

Mr. Ingalls was the Purple Emperor.

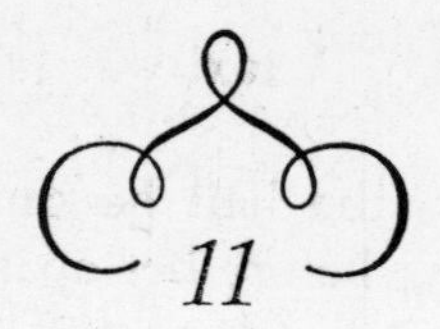

11

SPRING was squired in not by the first flower but by the first fly. It made noisy missions over Jean's head, reconnoitering the food she defended. She was laying out an imposing array of Brinkmann's specialties on both decks of the tea wagon borrowed from Joey Brent. Mrs. Marsan's left hand was still stubbornly wooden, and Jean had been coming in every morning since Friday, doing chores and caring for the puppies. Mrs. Marsan considered her hand almost a blessing, since it kept Jean busy.

The puppies were now famous, and Lady as well as Mr. Ingalls had passed through the strange alchemy which transmutes a citizen into a celebrity. Since the story of how she renounced a title for love appeared in Sunday's news, she had been receiving a continuous line of visitors. Nice people came in nice cars, with nice children. The puppies were all bought and paid for, at five dollars each, and Jean had the list of names and addresses, to notify when the personages were old enough to go to their new homes. All except Domino. Since Joey could not have him, he was for the Brinkmanns. A present. Mr. Brinkmann was as foolish as the twins about a dog, and for Domino, a career in a delicatessen such as Brinkmann's could hardly be bettered.

Mrs. Marsan came to the kitchen, carefully dressed in her brown georgette hostess, the studded squirrel rescuing the low V from any suggestion of immodesty. The neck fitted wryly, the sides drawn by the pin into an unwilling meeting, but it would never do to display the least trace of a cleft in the presence of a man of the cloth. Pastor Frankel was coming to lunch. When he wrote he wished to confer with her at her convenience on a matter of common concern, she had phoned him, fixing Thursday at noon. She had a special reason for wanting him for lunch, on Thursday.

"If I look as good as that noodle salad I'm satisfied," Mrs. Marsan said.

Jean turned around, swinging a hand at the fly. She was a little livelier today.

"You look fine. It doesn't show a bit you didn't put on corsets." She reconsidered. She found Mrs. Marsan's lips a trifle blue. "You might put on a smidge of lipstick though."

"Oh, God, no! . . . I've got to be modest, for a minister. It'd be different if it was a man coming."

The fly buzzed around Jean in low droning protests.

"I wish I could get rid of that pest." She threshed the air with her arms.

"That means news," Mrs. Marsan interpreted.

Despair shadowed Jean's face.

"The postman didn't bring anything this morning again. What do you think can have happened?"

Perhaps Eric had married Madam Blanche. Or perhaps he decided he wanted to be a bachelor forever. Or perhaps Jean had never mentioned that she was a widow *without* several children. Mrs. Marsan could produce a score of perhapses. But she commented only:

"I guess his letters were so dull he got tired of them himself. You'd have thought a man would write with more passion to his grandma."

"They showed such a lovely *character*," Jean said quietly.

Mrs. Marsan wished she could erase Eric the way you rub out a mistake in spelling. He was not only holding Jean back —when she had been so near the top of her climb—he was pushing her down. In the renewed fight against listless brooding Mrs. Marsan was determined not to let Jean slip an inch further, finding things to fill her every free minute, shoving her relentlessly off to her counter at Macy's. It was all the more aggravating considering that a girl like her could get barrels of letters if she wanted to—from young men with hair. Mrs. Marsan decided not to delay any longer. She would speak to Phil Cassidy today. . . .

"Better finish setting the tea wagon, dear."

Jean was standing there with a plate in her hand, looking at the wall. She resumed numbly, putting covers on things and spreading a napkin over the plateful of sliced *schwarzbrot*. The fly gave up and went to sit upside-down on the skylight, sullen and still.

Everything was ready now, and Mrs. Marsan had only to wheel in the wagon when the minister arrived. He was due any minute. Jean had to hurry out of her slacks into a dress and get off to work, but she still had time to give the puppies a drink. She put a soup plate down on the linoleum and sat beside it crosslegged, close to their box, which she had dragged in from the living room, since the minister was coming. Without discipline the dogs walked into the water and wallowed in it. She had to watch them.

When the bell rang Mrs. Marsan buzzed and went at once to the door. She wondered about The Correct Thing . . . In greeting a man of the cloth, she supposed it would be all right to shake hands warmly and say "Welcome!"

The caller was not in clerical clothes but in uniform. He had to juggle to take her outstretched hand because he was holding a large bouquet of American Beauties and his cap. Scanning her at a glance over the roses, he smiled, a good large smile—as of recognition—brightened by blue eyes.

"The man in the shop downstairs told me to ring the bell on the left. I found four buttons instead of one and I pushed them all. The other people must be out. Yours is the only one answered—and luckily it's right!"

The interrupted "Welcome!" was stuck in her throat, obstructing speech.

"I'm sorry to crash like this." He became uneasy before her glassy staring. "I should have written from Ostend, but I didn't have time. Leave offered suddenly and either I took it or waited months. Then we ran into a gale in the Dover Straits and had to put in at Folkestone. You weren't listed in the phone directory. I wanted to phone you when I phoned my people in Toronto. As soon as I arrived. Ship docked this morning."

"You're sure you rang the right bell?" She scrambled to fit him into a pale pattern of recollection.

"I'm looking for a Mrs. Landry, a widow. Aren't you—"

"Oh. You mean *Jean!* She's inside, on the floor. Come on in."

She knew now who he was. She remembered from the snapshot. Dan. Eric Arnold's friend. He was bringing news, a message. A last awful perhaps cracked open in her mind. Perhaps Eric was dead. And if he was, what would it do to Jean now. . . . Oh, God! She didn't mean that when she asked Jesus not to—

Jean put the puppies back in the box and got to her feet. Her eyes asked him about Eric, but he was unconscious of their questioning.

Deliberately he measured her from head to toe.

"That dress you sent . . ." he said huskily.

"It was mine," Mrs. Marsan told him.

Jean found a whisper for her fear. "Is Eric Arnold all right?"

"Yes, thank you. I'm fine."

He stood there looking at Jean, his bouquet forgotten, and she at him. They had nothing to say, but Mrs. Marsan could hear a swift torrent of wordless speech pouring in between them. *I thought Mrs. Landry was a lonely outsize elderly widow . . . I thought Eric's letters were so reserved because he was a middle-aged man with a mustache. . . .* Alarm went out of Mrs. Marsan on a giddy breath of relief, but her head was whirling.

At length he became aware of the long silence and groped for conversation.

"It's—I'm surprised to find such mild weather in New York, this time of year. It's—wonderful. Don't you think?"

Their eyes met again and locked.

"Today," Jean said softly, "is the first day of spring. . . ."

2

The air drew the curtains back, letting in the sun. If traffic noise and gas station smells crowded in with the better company, nobody seemed to mind. The table looked lovely, she thought, with the bowl of Eric's roses Jean had arranged before she went off with him, and the hand-painted Haviland, of course—let Adrian Larsch go to the devil—lent as always its gold-rimmed elegance.

Mrs. Marsan was flawlessly happy. She knew they made a picture: the minister in his frock coat and clerical collar; she in her georgette hostess; and Lady sitting beside the table washed and combed to cotton, wearing her new blue ribbon. It was all so genteel. . . .

Best of all, she observed, the nature of his mission in no way affected Pastor Frankel's appetite. He ate with enthusiasm, complimenting her coffee in parenthesis all during his preachment on the evils of falsehood. He was considerably shocked, he said, to learn that Miss Joey was not taking sewing lessons on Wednesday.

"We are especially and repeatedly warned against bearing

false witness. From Moses to Matthew. In Psalms and Proverbs. I have here a few helps I wrote down for you."

He rested his fork on his plate and reached into his pocket for his prayer book, extracting a neatly folded paper. Mrs. Marsan took it and skimmed the typewritten verses. *Thou shalt not raise a false report. . . . Deliver my soul, O Lord, from lying lips, or what shall be done unto thee, thou false tongue? . . . A false witness that speaketh lies, and he that soweth discord among brethren. . . .* There were many more.

"I'll read it some other time," she said, slipping it under her plate. "But I don't know about lying being bad. It's like dope."

"Yes?" Pastor Frankel accepted another from the plate of biscuits she passed him. "You say, like dope?"

"Well, it's bad in itself, but it has its uses. It eases the pain, in ugly operations."

He cleared his throat and changed the subject, going on to the next point as if he were speaking from notes. "When we are tempted to look into another's affairs, we must remember rather to be about our Father's business. How much more profitable it is in the end!"

"It wouldn't have been profitable to that man who was mugged if that Samaritan had minded his own business!" Mrs. Marsan laughed gaily, helping herself to butter.

"Allow me to suggest something for your daily reading."

He opened his prayer book again and drew out a paper typewritten on both sides, handing it to her gravely. She read without much interest: *A naughty person walketh with a froward mouth . . . frowardness is in his heart, he deviseth mischief continually. . . . Abide now at home; why shouldest thou meddle to thine hurt. . . .* She postponed reading the rest.

"We are likewise enjoined to watch the fruit of the mouth," the pastor continued. "Gossip is an abomination in the sight of God. It is written, The words of a talebearer are as wounds, and they go down into the innermost parts of the belly."

She was reminded to pass the platter of cold cuts. The roast beef sat rather well in the innermost parts, she thought. She surmised correctly that another paper would be forthcoming. *Keep thy tongue from evil, and thy lips from speaking guile. . . . A wholesome tongue is a tree of life: but perverseness therein is a breach in the spirit. . . . Death and life are in the power of the tongue. . . .* She looked up eagerly. "Do you keep a scrapbook?" she asked.

Pastor Frankel jumped as if the question had sprung out at him from a dark corner.

"Why, yes. Various trivia I like—"

"I'll send you some things from mine." She put her hand up before his forming protest. "No trouble at all."

"Another thing." He stirred his fresh cup of coffee, frowning at the tablecloth. "We should not waste our substance with riotous living. Gambling and that sort of thing, you know."

She waited for more verses but this time, magically, there were none.

"The only way to stop gambling—" she shrugged and sighed "—is not to give up riotous living, but to give up living at all. Everything everybody does is a bet. Even crossing the street. Lots of people lose. They get hit."

"A very limited point of view, my friend," Pastor Frankel said stiffly. "Tell me—" He arranged his knife and fork on the edge of his plate, refusing a third helping with a gesture. "Do you pray?"

Mrs. Marsan had to think. Did she?

"Of course!" she decided. "I read my favorite Watchword every day. It's something I cut out of the newspaper."

"A newspaper clipping!"

"It goes like this: *I expect to pass through this world but once—*" She was stalled. The idea was there, but the exact words were not. Funny, the way her memory was tricking her lately, hiding things and making her hunt for them. "I'll get it for you later. Anyway, the idea is, you're here only once—you've got to do what you can do while you can do it."

Pastor Frankel fell back as if struck. He was sitting in Mr. Cernak's chair and the arm came off. He retrieved it and fitted it back nervously.

"The sheerest Epicureanism!" His voice seemed louder for its shocked softness. "Don't you think at all of laying up for yourself treasures in heaven?"

Mrs. Marsan wondered why he took on so.

"I like to lay up a few pleasures on earth, too," she said.

"That's hedonism, madam."

She was surprised that Pastor Frankel pronounced words like Nick Dinapolis. Him a scholar and a preacher. . . . She saw no connection with heathenism in what she said, anyway.

"Believing that happiness is the sole end and aim of life, *are* you happy?"

That she could answer without hesitation.

"Yes, indeed! I was just saying the other day—I have no grudges against God. I'm happy."

"Scandalous. . . ." Pastor Frankel took out a handkerchief and sponged his jowls. "Positively immoral. . . ."

Mrs. Marsan was puzzled. Often you had to be immoral to be happy, but why was just being happy being immoral?

He gathered himself together. "Since you have all the happiness you want yourself, I trust you will not begrudge a little to Miss Edna Brent. You've made her very miserable. Do you realize what a hazardous thing it was, picking a man up out of the streets and bringing him into her sister's home?"

She wished she could remember what that was the Bible

said about going out into the highways and hedges to pick up people and bring them in. . . .

"Phil Cassidy's a grand young fellow. He wasn't a pick-up. He was a *find.*" She could remind him that Phil was Brenda Simms' brother but that fact might be more useful later.

"But I understand he has only one arm. He can't earn a living."

"He has a good job. Lots of men with *two* arms can't earn a living."

"We must consider Miss Joey's physical condition."

"As a minister you're supposed to be considering her spiritual condition." Mrs. Marsan was getting tired of his unreasonable reasoning. She took her stand firmly on the greatest premise in the dialectics of the church. "What's more important—body or soul?"

"*Soul,* of *course!*" The pastor was amazed to find himself answering such a question.

"Well, she don't wear braces on her soul."

The Reverend Frankel made a gesture with his hands as if he were lifting air.

"There seems to be nothing more I can do."

"Yes, there is." She slid a large piece of Viennese pastry on a pink glass plate and poured him more coffee. She got up and started for the door. "Phil's there now. You can marry them. They've got everything ready."

"I?" Pastor Frankel had risen, too. His face grew red as scarlet fever. Of whom he was thinking was evident even before he spoke. "You forget my duty to Miss Edna Brent as a member of my congregation!"

"I'm thinking of your duty to Mrs. Brenda Simms as a member of your congregation."

The pastor looked startled.

"Mrs. Simms has nothing to do with it."

"Hasn't she? She's as keen to see her brother married to

Joey and happy as Edna is to see her sister not married to him and miserable. And Brenda Simms has a temper twice as good as Edna's. You'll find out."

Mrs. Marsan paused, as if to indicate "Take your choice."

"I very much fear Miss Edna—" Pastor Frankel coughed nervously.

"We all do. But don't worry. By the time she finishes with *me,* she'll be too played out to work on you."

"Must it be today?" he parried. "There's time—"

"We schemed it for *now,*" Mrs. Marsan revealed. "While Phil's on his lunchtime and because Edna took today to work till evening, clearing up her desk before the trip."

The trip— Well, Edna could give the tickets to Phil and Joey for a honeymoon.

"Now just sit down and eat your dessert while I get them over," Mrs. Marsan concluded. "Mrs. Simms is there, too."

The wedding was lovely. What if the fly, seizing his chance, came down from the kitchen skylight to buzz about the remains of luncheon in the living room, and Lady's puppies, playing in their box by the stove, presented their idea of barking throughout the ceremony? And from outside rose the wheeze of a passing bus and the smack of closing auto doors over at the gas station, but over it all the marriage ritual rolled in a sonorous wave, out of the same little black book from which had lately come the typewritten sheets with Mrs. Marsan's lessons.

Joey was beautiful, her face shining like Phil's secret solitaire, which after this she could flash without a blasting "*What's that!*" from anybody. She wore a spray of pink rosebuds and lilies-of-the-valley pinned to the shoulder of her powder-blue suit. Phil beamed. He handled the rings as if they were the two greatest treasures in the world. And Brenda, plump and pretty in a gay spring print, looked so pleasant that Mrs. Marsan was afraid the reputation she had just given her as a hellcat would be ruined.

Why do people cry at weddings? Mrs. Marsan knew it was silly. She blinked back the tears and tried not to sniffle.

"What therefore God hath joined together—"

It was too late for Edna to do anything now, except raise a rumpus. Phil would phone the office the news and take the afternoon off. When Edna came home tonight he would be there with Joey to handle her.

"Oh, Phil, it might be awful." Joey looked more mischievous than worried. "Do you think we can do it?"

"Listen, honey," Phil said. "If we can lick old Mr. Can't-do each alone, what won't we be able to do to him together?"

3

It was after five o'clock and she was still answering the door. Every attempt to change from her cherished hostess into a careless kimono had been interrupted by callers—still people with children who wanted to see the dogs, and half an hour ago, Adrian Larsch. Adrian held a stack of books in the crook of her stunningly tailored arm. "I can never catch Mr. Ingalls at home," she said. "I wish you'd ask him to return these books to the library for me." *Why shouldest thou meddle. . . .* "He's too busy—he wouldn't have time," Mrs. Marsan feared sweetly. "But you might ask him yourself." Adrian thought writing notes was very convenient, didn't she? "Just slip a note under his door."

Now it was Mr. Ingalls himself. He came with the latest news of the Cernaks.

"I've gotten Mr. Cernak out on bail at last. He's gone right over to see his sister. All this secret agent scare we've been seeing in the papers complicated things."

"Good if Mr. Cernak could be scared. How's Jessamine?"

"The doctor is giving her thiamin hydrochloride. There are no brain lesions or psychoses—with the proper help she can be cured. What she needs more than medicine is a creative outlet. She's willing to teach. I'm trying to get her one of the studio apartments in Carnegie Hall."

"Misfortune's like manure," Mrs. Marsan said. "Sometimes good things grow out of it."

"She said to thank you for the box of sweet biscuits. They really did her good. People like her are used to quantities of sugar in their systems, and part of the treatment is to feed them sweets."

"That was a parcel post I got from Coral Sands." She wondered what about Coral. . . .

"I don't know why she should be having such chills," Mr. Ingalls continued. "The nurse says it's nothing, but it's darned uncomfortable."

"That always happens when she's without." Mrs. Marsan remembered all the shivering ends of months. "Wait a minute. I've got something that'll fix her." She fetched her sweater from the back of the chair in the bedroom. "She warms up when she wears this. It reminds her of the time she was Mamie in the opera."

She made a paper bag package of the sweater and gave it to Mr. Ingalls.

After he was gone, she felt strangely empty and forlorn. Soon they would all be gone. Coral and Vivien—already. Joey next, with Phil. Jean—she would probably end up in Toronto. Jessamine and Mr. Cernak moving to Manhattan. Mr. Ingalls off to England to look up things for a book about a long ago Sir Somebody-or-other. Nick Dinapolis— He always said women were undependable, but Jessamine was the supreme surprise. Though Mr. Ingalls paid the damages, Nick had the tavern up for sale. He was going to Florida to raise oranges.

She would miss them all, she thought, with a queer stab

in the chest that was almost like the familiar pain. Even Doc Kincaid. Even Adrian Larsch. Last Saturday morning she had seen Adrian's new luggage delivered—sleek, glossy pieces to be filled with fine, unfeeling stuff, like Adrian herself. Somehow they didn't look so gay. . . .

She was saddened, but not shaken, by these fluctuations. Hadn't her New Year's horoscope told her to watch March for changes? As she was remarking to Joey after the wedding, practically everything in the horoscope was fulfilled now, except the matter of money from a familiar but unexpected source, and the long journey. And Joey had sparkled, "Those things will come! Money and a journey—I'll bet anything that has to do with The Plantation!"

This time it was Sig. "I got to talk to you quick," he said. He came in and stood looking at the clock as if it were some fascinating instrument of torture. It was twenty-three minutes to six.

"I thought you said quick," Mrs. Marsan reminded.

Sig swallowed.

"It's about the opera glasses. We got to get them out of Sobel's today or they're sunk."

"You're crazy. You just brought them to him two weeks ago."

"That's it. He give me only two weeks on them. He says it don't pay him for his trouble—the way they come and go. Fact is, he's got an affection for them glasses—they been around him so much."

"For heaven's sake, go get them," Mrs. Marsan quailed. "You were quick enough to bring them there."

"I'm not got the money." Sig squirmed. "I tried to borrow it, but everybody says they just paid their income tax and they're cleaned out. They owe money themselves. Benny could let me have it Monday, but that's too far off."

"You ought to have something in the cash register!"

"Not enough. And Hannah howled. She don't believe me about the glasses."

Mrs. Marsan thought desperately.

"Phone Sobel and tell him you can't get there today—you'll bring him the money tomorrow."

"I phoned him that yesterday, the due date. He give me twenty-four hours' grace, and it's up."

"God's sake, why did you wait till *now* to tell me!" She knew Sobel—he meant what he said.

"I thought I could raise the money. Even Nick—he's not there."

"Doc Kincaid—he's always got money—"

Sig shrugged. "He'd rather lend me poison."

There was no arguing on that score.

"*Do* something!" Panic fastened on her, making her feel sick. "Don't stand there staring at the clock!"

"It's too late," Sig said miserably.

"You've got until nine!"

"That's on Saturday. Today's Thursday. He closes at six."

The minute hand jumped with a creak that was audible in the frantic silence. Twenty to.

"I've got a few dollars on me if you could make up the difference," Sig offered without much hope. "Have you got anything?"

"Twelve cents."

She had removed Lady's best ribbon before Sig came, and laid it over the back of Mr. Cernak's chair. Now her eyes, wildly running around the room, stumbled on it and stuck there. The new blue ribbon, bought for Lady as the most fitting present on her becoming a mother, held some meaning—some memory—some message that refused to crystallize in Mrs. Marsan's agitated mind. In that intense moment of strain she heard the baby barks of the puppies in the kitchen, and a lively adult yap. It was almost as if they had spoken to her. She remembered.

"Give me that ticket!" she said thickly. "I'll attend to this myself. I'm not trusting it to *anybody!*"

She rushed to the bedroom for her purse, its safety pocket rich with the fifty dollars the puppies' prospective owners had left on deposit. She had not intended touching it until the puppies were delivered, and then only in case of emergency. But circumstances had reversed her program. The emergency was now—the last act before the first.

Sig said, "You just got time if you don't miss the bus."

She was so nervous she couldn't get into her coat. She threw it over her shoulders and flew.

"Where're you getting the money?" Sig called over the balustrade.

She called back: "From Lady!"

4

She put the opera glasses in the top dresser drawer, with her tangled stockings and *Tess.* Three minutes more and she would have lost them. The whole thing was like a horrible dream, leaving a feeling of wonderment that she was awake and a vague nausea in readjusting to welcome reality. She would never pawn the glasses again—no, never. She swore it.

She wandered to the kitchen. Though it was supper time, she had no hunger, no energy even to drip a fresh pot of coffee. She drank what was left from noon, cold and strong and black, and felt depressed after it rather than revived.

The mad trip to Sobel's had tired her utterly. It had been too full a day—so much happening. Dragging to the living room, she sank on the sofa, half reclining in the corner. Her left arm hung over the end, and she found herself powerless to lift it without moving her whole body. It had turned to marble, something that belonged to a statue and not to her. She was too weary to wonder about it. She slumped there oddly exhausted, shapeless thoughts drifting through her mind like smoke.

There was something she ought to do. It came first as an urge, then grew into a whip, lashing her to action. She had known Mr. Cernak a long time—longer than she knew any of the others. She ought to write him a letter, explaining. . . .

She forced herself after pen and ink, searched foggily for paper. Fatigue sat on her mind like an iron lid, holding back the ability to think. She had a misty recollection of having had to borrow paper, of memorizing she should get some when she bought her new scrapbook, out of her next check. Suddenly the idea came of where she could find something to write on. She tore the sheet out, raggedly, the mutilated book looking familiar and foreign at the same time. I'm too worn out to recognize my own things, she thought.

Sitting at the bridge table, she began "Dear Mr. Cernak" and the words came out of her head clear and clean as she pulled all her strength together in concentration. Once she was interrupted. Somebody handed her a registered letter and she had to sign for it. Ordinarily she would have read it at once, but she had rushed enough for one day. It could wait till she finished what she had to say to Mr. Cernak.

She folded the sheet and went to put it in her dresser drawer, catch-all for important odds and ends. It jumped open lying there loose, so she placed it between the pages of *Tess*. Now she would read the registered.

She had difficulty opening the letter, her left hand refusing to help. Finally she got the scissors, and placing the envelope on the dresser, she weighted it down with the opera glasses and cut off the edge. As she shook out the contents, they swelled and swam before her eyes, a live white wave with a green lining. Money—or was it a check—attached. The wave receded and grew indistinct as she struggled with the clip. Lady barked at her side, a noisy nuisance. "Be quiet, Lady." Her tongue lifted up the words heavily.

The iron hand was closing in her chest, slowly, into the pitiless punching fist. She reached for the back of the chair where she always kept her sweater handy when she was not wearing it. It was gone.

The dresser drawer . . . maybe I put the bottle there. . . .

Her weight as she fell backward stripped the drawer out of place and it crashed to the floor, throwing out all it held. The bed caught her and she lay there crosswise, her legs hanging down over the side and an arm flung out above her head.

She who could never sleep—a good sleep at last. But why am I sleepy so early?

She was too tired to move, to open her eyes. Even the fist was tired now, tired of punching and crushing. The bed was a big boat, rocking cradlewise on an air ocean . . . so light, so restful. . . .

Be quiet, Lady. Bill . . . what's a banshee? The boat's stopped rocking. It's gliding straight ahead now. New country. New life. Exciting . . . adventure. . . .

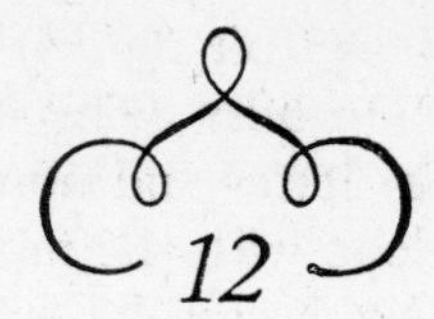

Mr. Cernak came by taxi to return the brown bottle Jessamine found in the sweater pocket. He received no answer to his knock beyond Lady's dismal wailing on the other side of the door.

"She *was* out," Sig said when Mr. Cernak asked him, "but she come back something like half an hour ago and I didn't see her go out again."

They opened the door with Sig's janitor key and Lady led them to the bedroom. Sig shook when he saw her. It had happened so quickly. . . . They lifted her legs into the bed and brought her arms against her sides. She looked almost tall, lying there in the long, soft brown georgette dress.

Mr. Cernak took her wrist. The plump flesh felt hard and cold. He said hoarsely, "It's too late, but I think the proper thing to do is get a doctor, anyhow." Sig went down to phone. He felt watery. He was glad to get away.

Mr. Cernak turned from the calm white face with the blue lids and lips. He saw the letter beside the opera glasses and went over to it. Registered. Two crisp bills were clipped to it, one for fifty and the other for five. He wondered if the letter contained news that could have caused a shock. Yet it was still folded; she might not have had time to read it. He opened it hesitantly and scanned a few lines. *Here's the fiver for the laundry and a fifty, your ten per cent on the* Louis XV *deal. Good work. I bet you could even sell a horse with a broken leg. . . .* He turned the page. *We're married a week already and leaving for Detroit today. Wondered if you deserved the biscuits, but too busy being happy to be technical.* . . . It was only a social letter and none of his business. He put it back in the envelope with the money.

While waiting for the doctor he set about gathering up the spill on the floor. He put the snarl of stockings back in the drawer and rewound the second-best length of blue ribbon he recognized as Lady's. The book in the bright jacket sent a wave of painful pleasure over him. His last gift to her. It always warmed him to see her going or coming from Joey Brent's with it, or to surprise her reading it at home. He picked it up and opened it, and his pleasure froze to consternation.

It was a minute before the indignant hurt wore thin enough for him to see the note he held. The note was for him. Scrawly and climbing on heavy unlined paper. His hand trembling, his eyes absorbed it in one lump. Jean, it said, would take care of the puppies until they were called for. When they were all delivered, she wanted Lady to go to Joey and Phil. All she had was the monthly check her husband had provided through an annuity. There never was any plantation —that was for Joey, but she wouldn't need it now. If anything happened, she'd like a genteel ceremony, with Pastor Frankel. She wanted to be sent back to her home town and buried in her family plot, in Three Rivers, Michigan. She had no relatives—she was the last of them all. . . .

Sig was back.

"The doctor'll be right over," he said.

Mr. Cernak felt dazed. Parts of the message were swirling around in his mind like straws in a whirlpool.

"She wants a—genteel ceremony," he heard himself saying.

Sig's eyes kept running incredulously to the figure on the bed and he kept dragging them back. This time the opera glasses caught and held them.

"I owe her fifty dollars. I never thought I'd be paying it back at her funeral." Something queer was happening inside of him. That muffled thumping was Happy Harry riding over his conscience with red-hot hoofs. "No—I owe her a hundred. That's right—one hundred dollars." I can get it from Benny —he said by Monday—

Mr. Cernak's eyes followed Sig's. The opera glasses. . . . He could pawn them. He'd heard of a ghoul named Sobel. . . . Or better, he would sell them to Sobel. They had been with her so much while she lived. This was a way they could still be with her. And Jessamine would be glad. . . . That with the money in the envelope—

"You'd better go down and wait for the doctor so he'll know where to come," he told Sig.

When Sig was gone he read the note again. Slowly, raw resentment boiled to fury within him. *There never was any plantation.* He tried to understand the maddening reference to Joey; it made no sense. All that made sense was the fact that he, Joseph Cernak, had been duped. Duped and tricked and trod on as thoroughly as any working worm had ever been by the moneyed class to which she made him think she belonged. She was an impostor, and as such she was party after all to the despicable stratum of society from which her message deposed her—the society of cheats and hypocrites. She, even as all of them, was like that smirking book, masking under a stolen, respectable cover. His indignation against the fact of deception confused and confounded in his mind with his rage against the people and policies which he believed poisoned the world, and he stood there shaking, the note ground to a ball in his hand.

Irresistibly he looked at her again, and the strange dignity of her utter stillness was water on his fire. The serenity of her face disturbed him. He felt suddenly as if he were looking at her for the first time. Somehow he was embarrassed. People were so unnaturally natural when they were—It was like looking at nakedness.

Calm again now, he kneeled down and smoothed out the crumpled note on the open book. About to fold the thick sheet as it was, he noticed on the other side a square of newsprint. He read it slowly, his lips moving silently over the words.

> **DAILY WATCHWORD**—I expect to pass through this world but once. Any good, therefore, that I can do, or any kindness that I can show to any fellow-creature, let me do it now. Let me not defer or neglect it, for I shall not pass this way again.

It seemed pasted there proudly, tenderly, set apart in solitary grandeur, as if it had been revered as a philosophy or a prayer.

He read it over, wondering, struggling to fit together into a comprehensible pattern the rough and smooth pieces of the things he knew about her. Something in the book open before him, heavily underlined and bracketed, came to his aid. "*The beauty or ugliness of a character lay not only in its achievements, but in its aims and impulses; its true history lay, not among things done, but among things willed.*"

He was still kneeling there, his face streaming wet under his skinny frail hands, when Sig came in with the doctor.

"The lady's husband?" the doctor asked quietly.

"No," Sig said, "just a friend."